P9-DFL-438

# language skills

# Writing in Action

## level d

LOYOLAPRESS.

**Managing Editor**      Kim Mason

**Production Manager**   Mary Bowers

**Editors**              Sandy Hazel, Jan Marcus, Margaret O'Leary

**Production Staff**     Phyllis Martinez, Kari Nicholls, Steve Straus

**Interior Design**      Mary Bowers

## Acknowledgments

*Every effort has been made to trace the ownership of all copyrighted material and to secure the necessary permissions to reprint selections. Any errors or omissions are unintentional and will be corrected in future printings.*

Images copyright © Photodisc 1997.

ISBN 0-8294-1007-4

©1997 Loyola Press
3441 N. Ashland Avenue
Chicago, Illinois 60657

The following pages © 2002 K12 Inc.:
Pages 1-34, 39, 42, 44-55, 64, 68, 69 (bottom), 72, 78-86, 101(bottom)-102

# WRITING TO A PROMPT

## What Is Writing to a Prompt?

Sometimes, you get to choose what to write about. When someone else tells you what to write about, you are writing to a prompt. Your mother may tell you to write a thank-you letter to your grandmother for a present. That is writing to a prompt. You may sit down to take a test that says, "Write about a place you like." That is writing to a prompt, too.

**A PROMPT is a topic you are asked to write about.**

A prompt might ask you to write one of several different types of essays. Some of these are:

### A Narrative Essay

A narrative tells a story. It may be fiction—a story with made-up characters. It may be nonfiction—for example, the story of your first overnight camping trip. A narrative has a beginning, a middle, and an end. Usually, you tell a narrative in the order in which the events happened.

### An Expository Essay

Expository is another word for explaining. In an expository essay, you may be asked to give information or explain something. For example, you might be asked to tell what your favorite sport is, and why.

*A Descriptive Essay*

In a descriptive essay, you describe a thing, person, event, or place. You might describe a room in your home. You might describe a storm. You try to make your reader see the place or thing. Sometimes, you want your reader to hear, smell, taste, and touch it, too.

*A Persuasive Essay*

To persuade is to try to get someone to agree with you. A prompt for a persuasive essay might ask, "Should children be given a regular allowance?" To write in response to that prompt, you need to think about what your opinion is. Then you write arguments to persuade your reader to agree with you.

## How to Tell the Kind of Prompt

When you are asked to write to a prompt, the first thing to do is decide what kind of essay you are being asked to write. Is it narrative, expository, descriptive, or persuasive? Knowing the kind of essay will help you do a better job of planning and writing the essay.

### When the Prompt Tells You Directly

Often, the prompt tells you exactly what kind of writing to do. For example:

Think back to a time when you were happy. What made you happy? Where were you? Who was there? What did you think, say, and do? Write a story that tells about this happy time.

When the prompt tells you to write "a story," then you know you need to write a narrative.

### Read for Clue Words

Sometimes, the prompt doesn't tell you exactly what kind of writing to do. When this happens, look for clue words in the prompt. Here are some:

NARRATIVE

Narrate . . .

Tell a story about . . .

Write about a time . . .

What happened when . . .

EXPOSITORY

Explain . . .

Tell why . . .

Talk about . . .

Write why . . .

PERSUASIVE

Should there be . . .

Convince others to . . .

Support your view that . . .

Persuade your readers that . . .

Make an argument that . . .

DESCRIPTIVE

Describe. . .

Tell about an object . . .

What does it look and feel like . . .

Write so your reader can see . . .

Picture in your mind . . .

### Prompts Without Clues

Not all prompts use the words you just read, but most do. Sometimes, there are no clue words. Then you have to decide what kind of writing do to. Here is a prompt without clue words:

*Write an essay about your favorite day of the week.*

When a prompt does not use clue words, it is often asking for an expository essay. For the prompt above, you would *explain* why a certain day of the week is your favorite.

### Which Type?

Here is an exercise to give you practice in deciding what kind of essay to write for a prompt. Write *narrative, persuasive, expository,* or *descriptive* on each line on the next page. Base your answers on the clue words you read. If there are no clue words, write what kind of writing you think the prompt is asking for.

1. Everyone has a favorite food. Describe your favorite food. Tell how it looks, tastes, and smells.

_____

2. Imagine that an animal could talk. Tell a story about an adventure you had with this talking animal.

_____

3. Your family is planning a vacation. Where would you most like to go? Write an essay that would persuade your family to vacation in that place.

_____

4. Which season is your favorite? Write an essay to tell why you like this time of year best.

_____

5. Who is your hero? Think of the person you admire the most. Then write an essay that convinces others to give this person an award for being a hero.

_____

6. Think about your favorite animal. Write an essay in which you give reasons for liking this animal best.

_____

# The Steps of Writing to a Prompt

Lee is a student who is about to take a test that asks him to write to a prompt. As you read what Lee does, notice the steps he goes through:

1. He decides what kind of writing the prompt is asking for.
2. He prewrites to help think of what he wants to say and plan his writing.
3. He writes a first draft.
4. He revises his writing.
5. He checks his grammar, punctuation, and spelling to correct any mistakes he made.

Here is what Lee reads when he opens the writing test booklet.

> Think of a day when something special happened to you.
> Write a story telling about what happened. You may write a story about something that really happened to you, or you may write a story that you make up. Be sure to write about the events in your story in detail.

Lee thinks:

> *First, I need to decide what kind of writing to do. Are there any clue words in this writing prompt? I see the words "write a story." That tells me this is narrative writing.*

Before he tries to write the essay, Lee does some prewriting. The prewriting helps him think of ideas and make a plan for what he will write.

To get started, Lee tries freewriting. He recalls several different special days that he has enjoyed and writes down as many ideas as he can think of. Because he is

freewriting, he does not worry about writing correctly. He just tries to get ideas on paper, like this:

surprise birthday party

camping trip—saw a grizzly bear

day I got my braces taken off

fishing trip with Uncle Mike

when we found the stray kitten

After looking over his freewriting, Lee decides to write about the day he went fishing with his uncle. To get started, he makes a list of the things that happened that day. He writes quickly, just to get lots of ideas on paper. Here is his list:

Uncle Mike picked me up really early—could hardly get out of bed!

It started raining.

We fished and fished, but didn't get anything.

We think about giving up—start to pack up the gear.

I catch a huge trout!

We cook it at home—a great dinner!

With his list finished, Lee can make a plan for writing. He knows he needs to include the following in his story:

1. An introduction that tells what he will be writing about

2. Paragraphs in the body to tell the story

3. An ending that brings the story to a satisfying close

Lee makes a quick outline. He puts the events in the order in which they happened. He includes an introduction and conclusion, like this:

1. Introduction—A special day with my uncle fishing
2. I woke up really early to get ready.
3. We got to the secret spot but didn't catch anything.
4. It started raining and we almost went home.
5. I caught a huge trout!
6. Mom cooked it—it was great.
7. Conclusion—it was a great day!

## Practicing Prewriting

Now you try it. On a separate sheet, practice prewriting for the prompt on the test that Lee is taking. Like Lee, you can prewrite in three steps:
1. Freewrite as many topics as you can think of.
2. Pick one topic and then write a list of ideas about that topic.
3. Write a quick outline.

Here again is the prompt:

Think of a day when something special happened to you. Write a story telling about what happened. You may write a story about something that really happened to you, or you may write a story that you make up. Be sure to write about the events in your story in detail.

## The First Draft

Now let's get back to what Lee is writing. With his outline to guide him, Lee writes a first draft about his day with his uncle. He skips a space between each line to leave room to make changes and corrections. Because he is writing quickly, he makes some mistakes. But he knows he will go back later to revise and proofread.

One relly fun day I remember was with my uncle Mike when we went fishing. Hes really a great uncle and when he asked me to go I was relly happy. So then we went.

I had to get up really early to go fishing with Uncle Mike. He said the place we were going fishing was far away and we needed to go really early. When I got up it was dark. My mom gave me some toast to eat and Uncle Mike said it was time to go and we were in the car and gone. We drove for a long time, up into the mountans to uncle Mike's secret spot. We parked the car and took all our stuff out,  the food for lunch and everything and we walked for a long time. Then we saw the stream.

It was still early and the water was dark. We set up our fishing things quietly so we wouldn't scare the fish. Then we began fishing and we fished and fished and fished. We were there for a long time. We ate lunch and still didn't catch any fish, but we talked and talked and that was as much fun as fishing. Then it began to rain. We thought about going. but we decided to stay a little bit longer because we relly wanted to catch a fish, so we did stay and a few mintues later, I got a fish on my line. It yanked my line and I pulled it. I thought it got away but I kept reeling it in and it was huge!

We brought the fish back to my house and my mom looked at it and she said it would make a good dinner. She cooked it for us and we ate it and it was delicious. That was such a fun day!

## The Revised Draft

When Lee looked at his work, he wasn't satisfied. He knew he could do better. He decided to revise.

Here is Lee's revised draft. Compare it with his first draft. What changes did he make to improve the essay?

Buzzzz went the alarm clock. It was still dark. I was about to go back to sleep when I remembered that today my Uncle Mike was taking me fishing. And today was sure to be really special because he was taking me to his secret fishing spot!

I had to get up so early because Uncle Mike's secret fishing spot was far away. Just as I finished my toast and juice, Uncle Mike poked his head in the door and called, "Rise and shine, sleepyheads! The fish are biting! Let's go!" And we were in the car and gone.

We drove high up into the mountains to Uncle Mike's secret stream. We parked the car and took out the fishing gear and a cooler with lunch and drinks. Then we walked downhill through tall trees. The air was cool and damp. It was so quiet all around us. As we walked, the sun began to come up. Then Uncle Mike whispered, "There's the stream!"

It was still early and the water was dark. We got our rods and reels ready very quietly so we wouldn't scare the fish. Then Uncle Mike showed me where to cast my line. We fished and fished for hours, but without any luck. We decided to take a break and eat lunch. As we ate, Uncle Mike and I talked and talked. That was as much fun as fishing. He told me about some of the big trout he had caught when he was a boy. He told me how he and my dad first found this secret fishing spot.

We were having a great time, and then it began to rain. We thought about going, but we decided to stay a little bit longer because we really wanted to catch a fish.

Finally Uncle Mike said, "Gee, I'm sorry, kid, but I think we have to pack up. Better start reeling in." So I started to reel in my line. And that's when I felt a sudden sharp tug. It almost yanked the rod right out of my hands. I held on tight and reeled it in.

"Steady now!" shouted Uncle Mike. "Not too hard!"

I kept reeling in, nice and easy. Then there was a flash of silver, and Uncle Mike scooped with his net and held up a huge, wiggling trout.

The rain was really pouring down now. Even though I was soaked, I smiled all the way home.

My mom cooked the fish for us. It was a delicious way to end a really special day!

### How Did Lee Do?

Remember, Lee wrote his essay for a test. His writing will receive a score. The scorers will be looking for certain things. They might use a checklist like this.

**Rate the essay from 1 (lowest) to 4 (highest) on each of the following:**

*Organization*

_____ The essay has a beginning, middle, and end.

_____ The essay moves smoothly from one event to the next.

_____ A reader can follow the events of the narrative.

*Focus*

_____ The topic of the story is clear.

_____ The writer stays on subject.

_____ All paragraphs and sentences help tell the story.

*Language*

_____ The sentences are interesting and varied.

_____ The writer uses well-chosen details.

_____ Words paint a good picture and are used correctly.

_____ Dialogue, if used, adds to the story.

*Conventions*

_____ Sentences are complete.

_____ Grammar is correct.

_____ Punctuation and capitalization are correct.

_____ Spelling is correct.

# LESSON 3

# Writing to a Narrative Prompt

Do you remember what a narrative prompt asks you to do?

A narrative prompt asks you to tell a story. The prompt might tell you if the story has to be real or made up. Lee wrote his essay in response to a narrative prompt.

If a prompt asks you to write a narrative, here are the main points to keep in mind.

## What to Include in a Narrative

Persuasive, expository, and descriptive essays are all organized around a series of ideas or main points. But narrative writing tells a story, and generally, the best way to tell a story is to write from the first event to the last one, in order.

### Stay in Focus

The whole story should focus on one main event, just as Lee's essay focused on the special day that he went fishing with his uncle. Each paragraph should focus on a single smaller event that is part of the main story. Within each paragraph, all the sentences should be about that event. Each step of the story should be clear. One event should lead to the next.

### Good Details and Descriptions

Precise details and descriptions are important in any kind of writing. That goes for narrative writing, too. Make sure to describe how people look and sound. When you describe places and things, think about how they look, sound, smell, and feel. Try to make your reader see "a movie in her mind." You want to *show*, *not tell*, your reader what happened. You can do that by offering precise details and descriptions.

For example, consider these passages from Lee's draft and his final essay:

**Telling** (from Lee's draft): *We walked for a long time.*
**Showing** (from Lee's revised essay): *Then we walked downhill through tall trees. The air was cool and damp. It was so quiet all around us.*

*Use Dialogue*

Here is a passage from Lee's draft:

*Uncle Mike said it was time to go and we were in the car and gone.*

Compare that with what Lee wrote when he revised his essay:

*Uncle Mike poked his head in the door and called, "Rise and shine, sleepyheads! The fish are biting! Let's go!" And we were in the car and gone.*

Which passage better shows your reader what happened? By using dialogue, the second passage puts your reader into the action. It lets him hear what happened.

Look back at Lee's revised essay on pages 8-9 and see where else he added dialogue.

**WRITER'S WORKSHOP** When you write DIALOGUE, remember these three rules:
1. Put the words each speaker says within quotation marks.
2. Punctuation marks such as commas and periods almost always go inside the quotation marks.
3. Begin a new paragraph each time a different person starts to speak.

## Writing to a Narrative Prompt: A Practice Essay

Now you will practice writing to a narrative prompt. Go through each of the following steps:

1. *Identify that the prompt asks for a narrative.*

Look for the clue words *narrative, story, tell about a time*, or *tell what happened*. Those words tell you that the prompt is asking for a narrative.

Read these two prompts. Write *narrative* in front of the narrative prompt.

_____ You have enjoyed spending time with many different children. Choose one of these children and tell a story about a time you enjoyed with him or her.

_____ Everyone has a place he or she likes best. Write about that place, describing what you like about it, where it is, and when you go there. Write so that your reader can see, feel, smell, and hear the place.

2. **Plan your writing.**

You will be writing to this prompt:

*You have enjoyed spending time with many different children. Choose one of these children and tell a story about a time you enjoyed with him or her.*

First, try freewriting to decide what to write about. Write in the space below. Don't worry about writing correctly—just get down some possible topics.

_____

_____

_____

_____

_____

_____

_____

_____

Now look back at your freewriting. Which topic do you like best? Circle it.

After Lee picked his topic, he made a list of ideas related to his topic. You can make a list as well, or you can try another approach. Remember, a narrative is a story. A story needs characters, a setting, and a plot. You can write each of those words on a sheet of scratch paper, and then list your ideas as a chart. For example, here is a chart made by a girl named Maya:

| CHARACTERS | SETTING | PLOT |
| --- | --- | --- |
| me | winter | We decide to put on a play. |
| Sarah | basement | We decide to do Red Riding Hood. |
| Jay | | We get other kids. |
| Sarah's sister | | We practice the play. |
| | | Everybody comes and it's great! |

In the space below, write ideas related to your topic. You can write a list like Lee or a chart like Maya.

_____

_____

_____

_____

_____

Now that you have ideas for your narrative, you need to organize them and plan your essay.

To plan his essay, Lee wrote this quick outline, with the events in order:

1. Introduction—A special day with my uncle fishing

2. I woke up really early to get ready.

3. We got to the secret spot but didn't catch anything.

4. It started raining and we almost went home.

5. I caught a huge trout!

6. Mom cooked it—it was great.

7. Conclusion—it was a great day!

You can write a quick outline, or you can use a plan like the one below. In this plan, you list each event in order, and then you write one or two details about each event. You can also make notes about where you think dialogue would work well.

First event: _____

   detail _____

   detail _____

↓

Second event: _____

   detail _____

   detail _____

↓

Third event: _____

   detail _____

   detail _____

In the space below, either write a quick outline, or make a diagram like the one on the previous page.

3. *Write a first draft.*

If you look at Lee's two drafts, you can see that in his first draft he did not worry too much about spelling or grammar. He knew he could work on those later.

On a separate sheet of paper, write your first draft. Follow your plan as you write. Write on every other line so that you have room to revise later. Here is the prompt again:

*You have enjoyed spending time with many different children. Choose one of these children and tell a story about a time you enjoyed with him or her.*

4. *Revise your work.*

In this step, take a good look at the draft you wrote. Try to think of ways to improve it. Use these questions to guide you as you revise:

- Does your introduction catch your reader's interest and tell what you will be writing about?
- Does the body develop the story, with each paragraph telling about a different event?
- Are there places where you can add detail or dialogue to help your reader see "a movie in his mind"?
- Does your conclusion wrap up the story for your reader?

5. *Proofread and make a final clean copy.*

The last step is to make a clean final copy and then carefully proofread to make sure there are no errors. Look at spelling, grammar, punctuation, and capitalization. When you have checked every sentence and made all the corrections, you're finished!

### How Did You Do?

Here is a checklist that scorers might use to evaluate a narrative essay.

**Rate the essay from 1 (lowest) to 4 (highest) on each of the following:**

*Organization*

____ The essay has a beginning, middle, and end.

____ The essay moves smoothly from one event to the next.

____ A reader can follow the events of the narrative.

*Focus*

____ The topic of the story is clear.

____ The writer stays on subject.

____ All paragraphs and sentences help tell the story.

*Language*

____ The sentences are interesting and varied.

____ The writer uses well-chosen details.

____ Words paint a good picture and are used correctly.

____ Dialogue, if used, adds to the story.

*Conventions*

____ Sentences are complete.

____ Grammar is correct.

____ Punctuation and capitalization are correct.

____ Spelling is correct.

# Writing to an Expository Prompt

In some ways, writing an expository essay is like writing a narrative. In both types of writing: (1) you make your writing as well-organized and clear as you can; (2) you have a beginning, a middle, and an end; (3) you stick to the topic; and (4) you make sure the conventions (grammar, spelling, capitalization, and punctuation) are correct.

But while a narrative essay tells a story, an expository essay gives information or explains. In an expository essay, you aren't trying to persuade someone or make him believe you are right—that's what you do in a persuasive essay. You aren't just trying to describe—that's what you do in a descriptive essay.

Here are examples of prompts for expository essays:

• Explain why a person in your life is special.

• What one thing would you change to make this country a better place to live?

• Name a book you have read that you greatly enjoyed, and explain why.

## Developing Expository Paragraphs

In a narrative essay, each paragraph develops an event in a story. But in an expository essay, each paragraph focuses on a single idea, supported by details.

In expository essays, most paragraphs have three parts:

1. The topic sentence
2. The body (details and supporting information)
3. A closing sentence

### 1. *The Topic Sentence*

In an expository essay, every paragraph should have a main idea. This main idea is stated in a topic sentence. The topic sentence tells what the paragraph is going to be about. Especially when writing for a prompt, it is a good idea to write the topic sentence as the first sentence of the paragraph.

## 2. *The Body*

The sentences that follow the topic sentence make up the body of the paragraph. These sentences give information about the main idea. They add details to support the topic. All of the sentences should be about the main idea stated in the topic sentence.

## 3. *The Closing Sentence*

In some paragraphs, the last sentence works as a closing sentence. A closing sentence wraps up a paragraph by calling attention to the main idea announced in the topic sentence. A closing sentence is often an echo or a reflection of the opening sentence. The closing sentence should be the thought or idea that you want the reader to remember most.

Read this paragraph from an expository essay written in response to this prompt: "Explain why a person in your life is special."

Most of all, my grandmother is wise. She can look at me and see right away that I have something on my mind I need to talk about. She knows when not to talk to me, too. She has a story or saying about every topic. She can talk about how saving money is important, and how sad it is to have a fight with a friend. My grandmother is more than smart—she is wise.

Now read the paragraph again, and this time identify the topic sentence, the body, and the closing sentence.

## Steps to Writing to an Expository Prompt

Follow these steps to write to an expository prompt.

### 1. *Decide if you should write an expository essay.*

When you are reading the prompt, look for key words such as *tell about* and *explain.* These words signal that you should write an expository essay

Which of the following prompts asks you to write an expository essay? Write expository in the blank in front of the expository prompt.

_____ Everyone has wanted to be a hero. Maybe you have been a hero. Tell about a time in which you were a hero, or write a story you make up in which you are the hero. Tell what happened, and what made you heroic.

_____ What person has been most important in your life? Write about the person who has made the most difference in your life. Tell why you think this person has been so important.

2. ***Plan your expository essay.***

The prompt about the person who is most important in your life is asking for an expository essay. Think of the person you want to write about. Write that person's name at the top of a piece of scratch paper, and then freewrite whatever comes to mind.

Now think about three or more main points you want to make, and what details will support each of these points. Fill in the web below with that information.

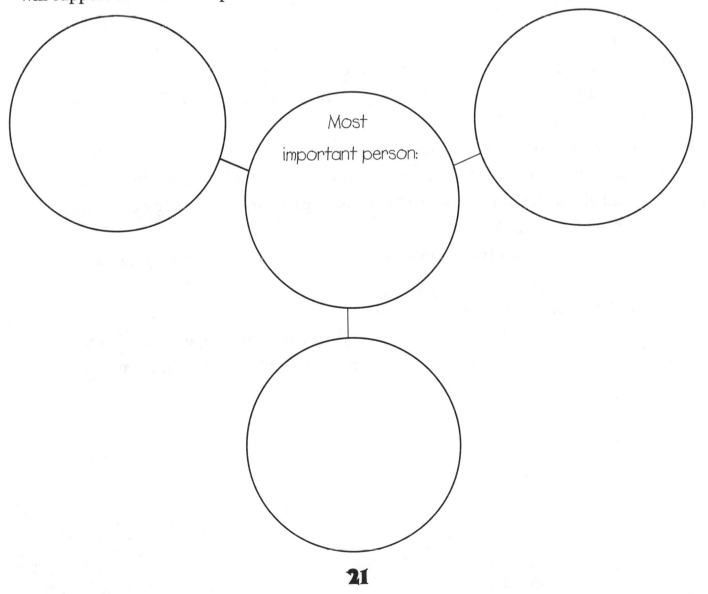

Most important person:

3. *Outline your essay.*

On a sheet of paper, make a quick outline of what you want to write. Use your web. In your outline, include these things:

- Your introduction
- The body, which should have at least three main ideas
- The conclusion

4. *Write your first draft.*

Write your first draft on a separate sheet of paper. Follow your outline as you write. You may want to write the body of your essay first, and then add the introduction and conclusion. Remember that you will be revising your first draft. Write on every other line so that you have room to revise what you write.

5. *Revise your essay.*

Keep these questions in mind as you revise your essay:

- Does your introduction tell what you will be writing about? Does it catch your reader's interest?
- Does the body develop each main point in a paragraph? Does each paragraph start with a topic sentence? Is each topic sentence followed by details that tell about that topic sentence? Does each paragraph in the body end with a closing sentence?
- Does your conclusion wrap up what you want to say in a satisfying way?

6. *Proofread your essay.*

Make a clean final copy of your essay. Then check your paper to catch and correct any errors. Look carefully at spelling, punctuation, capitalization, and grammar.

## How Did You Do?

Here is a checklist that scorers might use to evaluate an expository essay.

**Rate the essay from 1 (lowest) to 4 (highest) on each of the following:**

*Organization*

____ The essay has an introduction, body, and conclusion.

____ The essay moves smoothly from point to point.

*Focus*

____ The subject is clear, and the writer stays on subject.

____ All paragraphs and sentences relate to subject of essay.

____ Paragraphs have a main idea and supporting details.

____ There is enough information to explain the topic.

*Language*

____ The sentences are interesting and varied.

____ The writer uses specific, well-chosen details.

____ Words are vivid, strong, and used correctly.

*Conventions*

____ Sentences are complete.

____ Grammar is correct.

____ Punctuation and capitalization are correct.

____ Spelling is correct.

# Writing to a Descriptive Prompt

In a descriptive essay, you describe a thing, person, event, or place. You might describe a room in your home. You might describe a storm. You try to make your reader see the place or thing. Sometimes, you want your reader to hear, smell, taste, and touch it, too.

An expository essay or a narrative essay may include some description, and many of the best do. For example, if you are writing a story, you will want to describe how characters look or what the setting is like. In a descriptive essay, however, the focus of the writing is almost entirely on description.

Here are two prompts for descriptive essays:

- Imagine that you have to explain a food you enjoy to someone who has never seen or tasted it. You may want to describe tastes, sights, sounds, and smells in your essay.

- Everyone has a possession he or she loves. It may be an old blanket or a catcher's mitt. It may be a pair of jeans that fit you just right. Picture that possession in your mind. Now, describe it for your reader so he or she will be able to picture it clearly.

## Organizing Writing to a Descriptive Prompt

You might organize a descriptive essay about a special possession this way:

- Paragraph 1: An introduction that tells what the possession is and why it is important to you.
- Paragraphs 2-4: One paragraph that explains what it looks like, one paragraph that explains what it feels like, and a third paragraph on some other feature or qualities.
- Paragraph 5: Conclude with an ending paragraph in which you summarize the descriptions of the possession.

In a descriptive essay, a paragraph in the middle of the essay would contain a topic sentence that gives a description, and the other sentences would back up that description with details. Here is an example of a paragraph that might appear in an essay about a favorite blanket.

> I know this blanket is old. I've had it since I was born, and that is one of the reasons it is so special to me. The blanket started out green, but now it's sort of a faded mint color. Over the years my mom has tried to fix the many holes in it. It is so old, though, that now there are almost more patches than blanket. This poor old blanket has been through a lot—after all, it's as old as I am!

Notice that this paragraph focuses on details about how *old* the blanket is. How does the writer help us see the blanket?

## Steps to Writing to a Descriptive Prompt

Follow these steps to write to a descriptive prompt.

### 1. *Decide if you should write a descriptive essay.*

Look for key words and phrases such as *describe* and *tell how it looks, smells, and sounds*. Those words tell you that you will be writing a descriptive essay.

Which of the following prompts asks you to write a descriptive essay? Write descriptive in the blank in front of the descriptive prompt.

_____ Think of a place that is special to you. It may be inside your house, or in a park. It may be in your bed, or at a friend's house. Describe this special place. Tell what it looks, sounds, smells, and feels like to be there.

_____ Imagine you want a gift for your birthday. Write an essay to convince your parents to buy you this gift. Give reasons that would persuade your parents.

2. *Plan your essay.*

To write to the descriptive prompt about a special place, think of how you would describe that place. You can start by freewriting to get down some ideas. Then think of three main points about that special place.

You can make a web with "My special place" in the center, and bubbles with how it looks, another about how it smells, and a third about how it sounds or feels. (You can organize the paragraphs in a different way if you want to. Just be sure each paragraph focuses on one point.) Write details in each bubble that support each of these points.

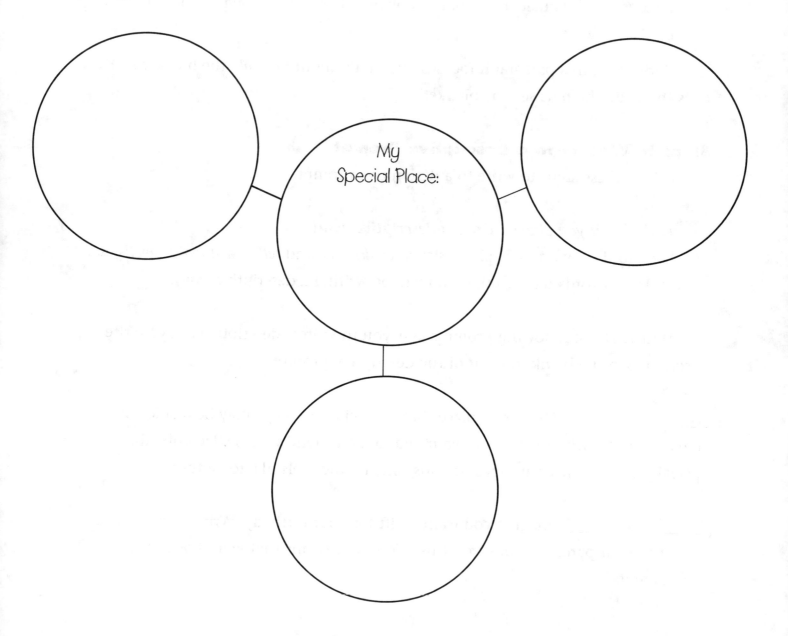

3. **Write a quick outline.**

Use your web to make an outline that has an introduction, at least three paragraphs for the body, and a conclusion.

4. **Write your first draft.**

Write your first draft on a separate sheet of paper, following your outline.

5. **Revise your essay.**

Look at your introduction, body, and conclusion. Is your essay well-organized? Do the paragraphs in the body have a topic sentence, supporting sentences, and a closing sentence? Are there places where you could provide more detail, or add colorful adjectives?

6. **Proofread your essay.**

Make a clean final copy of your essay. Then check your paper to catch and correct any errors. Look carefully at spelling, punctuation, capitalization, and grammar.

## How Did You Do?

Here is a checklist that scorers might use to evaluate a descriptive essay.

**Rate the essay from 1 (lowest) to 4 (highest) on each of the following:**

*Organization*

____ The essay has an introduction, body, and conclusion.

____ Each paragraph adds something new to the description.

____ The essay proceeds smoothly from point to point.

*Focus*

____ The description paints a detailed picture of the subject of the essay.

____ The writer stays on subject.

____ All paragraphs and sentences tell about the subject of essay.

*Language*

_____ The sentences are interesting and varied.

_____ The writer uses specific, well-chosen details.

_____ Words are vivid, strong, and used correctly.

*Conventions*

_____ Sentences are complete.

_____ Grammar is correct.

_____ Punctuation and capitalization are correct.

_____ Spelling is correct.

# Writing to a Sample Prompt

You can try writing to a prompt that might appear on a writing test. Before you begin, keep these points in mind:

1. Decide what kind of writing the prompt is asking for—watch for the clue words.

2. Think about what you want to write. Freewrite to help get your ideas flowing. Choose a topic you will be able to write about for several paragraphs.

3. Plan your writing, using whatever method you like best. You could try making notes, a list, a web, or a diagram. If you are writing an expository, persuasive, or descriptive essay, include the supporting details that will support your main points. If you are writing a narrative essay, plan a paragraph for each event.

4. Double space your first draft. Don't worry about grammar or spelling when you write. Just get your ideas down.

5. Revise for organization and ideas.

6. Proofread to correct any errors in spelling, punctuation, capitalization, and grammar.

Here is the prompt for the sample writing test:

*Many people have a favorite season or time of year. Think about your favorite season, and why it is your favorite. Write an essay explaining why this season is your favorite.*

You can use the next two pages to plan and to write a rough draft of your paper. Use the other pages to write your final copy.

**Rate the essay from 1 (lowest) to 4 (highest) on each of the following:**

*Organization*

_____ The essay has an introduction, body, and conclusion.

_____ The essay proceeds smoothly from point to point.

_____ The writer uses transitions when necessary.

*Focus*

_____ The subject is clear, and the writer stays on subject.

_____ All paragraphs and sentences relate to subject of essay.

_____ Each paragraph has a main idea and supporting details.

*Language*

_____ Sentences are interesting and varied.

_____ The writer uses specific, well-chosen details.

_____ Words are vivid, strong, and used correctly.

*Conventions*

_____ Sentences are complete.

_____ Grammar is correct.

_____ Punctuation and capitalization are correct.

_____ Spelling is correct.

# LESSON 1

## PREWRITING: What Is a Persuasive Paper?

Every time you turn on the TV or pick up a newspaper, someone is trying to PERSUADE you to buy or to do something. Do you have an opinion or a belief that you would like to share with someone else? If so, you probably want to CONVINCE them to believe the same way you do.

In this unit, you'll get a chance to speak your mind. You'll get to tell others what you believe—and why you believe it. You'll do this by writing a PERSUASIVE PAPER.

For every opinion you have, someone else might disagree with it. An OPINION is what someone believes to be true. Different people believe different things. That's why you need facts and good explanations to back up your opinions. This will help convince someone else to agree with you. Below are some facts and some opinions. Put an F in the blank beside each fact. Put an O beside each opinion.

_____ 1. Spring is the best season.

_____ 2. Tulips bloom in the springtime.

_____ 3. Carrots are vegetables.

_____ 4. Cats make better pets than dogs.

_____ 5. Children watch too much TV.

_____ 6. The earth is round.

_____ 7. Our cities should be kept cleaner.

_____ 8. Yellowstone National Park has bears.

_____ 9. Bees make honey.

_____ 10. Girls should be allowed to play football.

To write a good persuasive paper, there are two things to remember:

1. State your opinion clearly.

2. Use facts, personal experiences, and explanations to back up your opinion.

**WRITER'S WORKSHOP**

A PERSUASIVE PAPER is a report that expresses an opinion and backs it up with facts, personal experiences, and explanations.

Think about the report you wrote earlier this year. The steps you followed are printed below, but they are scrambled. Number them in the right order.

_____ Take notes as you gather information.

_____ Look for sources of information about your topic.

_____ Organize your facts into an outline.

_____ Choose a topic and narrow it.

_____ Revise your report.

_____ Write a first draft.

You will use these same steps to prepare your persuasive paper. You'll also do it the same way you wrote the report: one step at a time.

☑ Look in the newspaper or in a magazine. Find an ad or a message trying to convince you to do something. What does it want you to do? What reasons does it give to persuade you?

_____

_____

# PREWRITING: Choosing and Narrowing a Topic

A persuasive paper gives you a chance to convince (or *persuade*) others that an opinion of yours is true. It gives you the stage and puts your ideas in the spotlight. The first step is to think of some opinions that you believe are important. Here is a list that a girl named Gwen made:

I think that <u>girls should be allowed to play all sports.</u>

I believe that <u>people should wear helmets when they ride bikes.</u>

In my opinion, <u>everyone should have a pet.</u>

Use the lines below to list some ideas you could write about in a persuasive paper. Remember that you must back up your opinions with facts and personal experiences.

I think that _____

_____.

I believe that _____

_____.

In my opinion, _____

_____.

☑ Choose one of your three opinions as the topic for your persuasive paper. Put a

✓ beside the topic you've chosen.

## Narrowing Your Topic

Writers sometimes choose topics that include too many ideas for a single paper. It would take too long to write about them. We say that these topics are too "wide."

Below are some topics for persuasive papers. Some of them are too wide, but others have been narrowed. Put an N beside the most narrow topic in each group.

1. ____ Air, soil, and water pollution are bad for our planet.

   ____ Americans should end pollution.

   ____ Our town should start a program to recycle aluminum cans, glass, and paper.

2. ____ All Americans should know foreign languages.

   ____ All students in the United States should learn Spanish.

   ____ Americans should learn more about other cultures.

Let's try narrowing some topics. Read each topic on the left below. Then use the blank lines to write one part of the topic. Be sure that the part is small enough to write about in a short paper. The first topic has been narrowed for you.

| Wide Topic | Narrow Topic |
|---|---|
| Pets are good for people. | A dog is a faithful friend. |
| Exercise is healthful. | |
| | |
| Kids learn things from TV. | |
| | |

☑ Now look at the topic you chose on page 37. Does it need to be narrowed? If so, think of one part of your topic and write it here:

_____

(Your Narrowed Topic)

# PREWRITING: Thinking About Sources

You've chosen and narrowed your topic. Now it's time to gather the facts you need to back up your opinion. A good place to start is with your personal experience.

## Personal Experience

Let Gwen tell you about an event that led to her topic: "Children should have to wear helmets when they ride bikes."

One day last summer I was waiting for my friend Mara to come over. From my front porch I saw her coming down the street on her bike. She was about a block away. And then, just as Mara crossed a driveway, a car backed out. I saw the car hit her back wheel. She flew off the bike and hit her head. I ran to her as fast as I could. She was scraped and bruised and crying. But she was all right, because she was wearing a helmet. That helmet saved her life.

✓ If you have had personal experiences that back up your opinion, describe them briefly on the lines below:

_____

_____

_____

_____

_____

_____

## Research

Of course, your own experience is not the only way to back up your opinion. You'll also want to use facts from books, magazines, and reference materials. You may want to include experiences that others have had. Getting the information you need from these sources is called RESEARCH.

**WRITER'S WORKSHOP**

**Looking for information in sources is called RESEARCH.**

Below are three kinds of research activities. You may remember some of them from other writing projects:

| | |
|---|---|
| **Interviewing** | asking people (usually experts) for facts and personal experiences to support your opinion. |
| **Using the Library** | Looking for information in books, magazines, and reference materials. |
| **Searching the Internet** | Looking for reliable websites with trustworthy information on your topic. |

## Interviewing

If you identify someone to interview who has knowledge or experience of your topic, follow these tips:

• Call the person and briefly explain the essay you are writing. Ask politely for his or her time, and set up a time for an interview on the phone or in person.

• In advance, prepare a list of 3-5 questions to ask. Of course you might think of other questions to ask during the interview.

• Take a small writing pad and at least two pens or pencils to the interview.

• Make sure to get the correct spelling of the person's name, and his or her correct title.

• During the interview, write down key words and phrases that tell the main points the person is making.

• If you think you will want to use the person's exact words in your essay, then be sure to write exactly what he or she says. Read the quotation back to the person to make sure you have written it accurately.

• Thank the person for his or her time in answering your questions.

• Ask for permission to call the person again if you have any follow-up questions.

Can you think of a good person to interview? If so, write his or her name here.

_____

## Using the Library

When you wrote a report, you learned how to find information in the library. You learned how to use a card catalog and a computer catalog to locate books, encyclopedias, and magazines.

When you find a source that looks useful for your persuasive paper, begin a note card on it. On the card, write the title and the name of the author (if it is given). Also:

• If the source is a book, write the call number.

• If the source is a magazine, write the date.

• If the source is an encyclopedia, write the volume number or letter.

On each card, write the numbers of the pages on which you find the information you need.

Look at these examples:

Safety on Your Bicycle                J 796.6
by Lucia Raatma
see pages 12, 13-15, 24

"Cycling to Victory"
Outdoor Adventures
July 2001
pages 21-24

The New Book of Knowledge, Vol. 2 (B).
pages 30-34

☑ Before you start the next lesson, try to find at least two sources with information on your topic. Write down the required information on note cards.

### Searching the Internet

With the help of an adult, you can also search the Internet for information on your topic.

The Internet has a lot of information, but you have to be very careful to be sure you are getting good information.

When you find a reliable source with good information, write down the name of the site, the URL (the Internet address) of the specific page or pages you use, and the date you visit the site. For example:

*Name of Site*: National Safe Kids Campaign
*URL*: http://www.safekids.org/index.cfm
*Date*: February 17, 2002

Is there a website that looks like it has good information on your topic? If so, write the name and URL here:

Name: _____

URL: _____

Date: _____

# PREWRITING: Gathering and Organizing Information

## Choosing Subtopics

As you read your sources, you will find that some facts belong together in subtopics. A subtopic is a group of facts about one special part of a topic.

As you read your sources, look for two or three subtopics. These will probably be the points that come up most often in your sources.

While reading about bicycle safety, Gwen decided on these subtopics:

1. Facts about bicycle accidents

2. Facts about how helmets save lives

3. Helmet laws needed in all states

When you have decided on your subtopics, write them on the lines below.

1. _____

2. _____

3. _____

As you do research and take notes, you might find a new subtopic or decide to change one of your subtopics. That's fine. Writers often make such changes as they learn more about their topics.

## Taking Notes

As you read your sources, you'll need to take good notes on note cards. Try to write at least two note cards for each of your subtopics. Remember these rules:

1. At the top of each note card, write the subtopic the notes are about.
2. Only write notes about one subtopic on each card.
3. In general, you should not copy from your sources. Try to put the facts in your own words.
4. If there is a good reason for using the exact words from a source, then write those words in quotation marks. For example:

You might think that bike helmets are only for serious riders. But the Bicycle Helmet Safety Institute says, "Nasty bicycle crashes can happen to anyone, anytime, anywhere, and at any speed."

Here is part of a paragraph that Gwen found on a website. Use this paragraph to practice taking notes. On the note card on the next page, make notes about the paragraph in your own words.

A bicycle helmet can't keep someone from falling off a bike. It can't keep a car from hitting you. But it can cut the chances of serious brain injury. It does this by cushioning the blow that otherwise would hit the skull and brain in a crash.

Bicycle Helmet Campaign Guide     Feb. 12, 2002

http://www.bhsi.org/manual.htm

## Opposite Opinions

As you do research, you are looking for information to support your opinion. But you will probably find information that supports the opposite opinion as well.

Do not ignore these opposite opinions. Take notes on the strongest opinions against what you believe. (You will use these notes in the next lesson.) To be really persuasive, you will need to show that you understand the arguments against you, but that your argument is stronger.

☑ Now take notes from your sources. Remember to write the information in your own words or put quotation marks around any words you copy exactly from a source.

# PREWRITING: Seeing the Other Side and Planning the Paper

## Seeing the Other Side

Gwen believes very strongly that children should have to wear bike helmets. But while she was doing research, she found some articles and websites that argued against her opinion.

Her first reaction was, "That's silly. They're just plain wrong." But she knew that in her paper it would not be a good idea to say that people who disagree with her are "silly" or "wrong." She knew that she had to treat opposite opinions with respect, even if she strongly disagreed with them.

When you write a persuasive essay, it is a good idea to show that you are aware of the main arguments against your opinion. Don't try to attack those arguments. Just calmly state them. Then go on to show why your opinion is better.

For example, Gwen found one source that said it takes away a person's freedom if he or she is required to wear a helmet while riding a bike. Gwen read the argument carefully, then she put it in her own words, like this:

There are some people who say that no one should force them to wear bike helmets. They say that it should be their decision whether or not to wear helmets. It is true that a law that makes children wear bike helmets does take away some freedom.

Notice that Gwen did not say this opinion is "wrong" or "silly." She even said that it is true. This shows that Gwen is a reasonable person who can understand why some children might think they should not be required to wear bike helmets. But then Gwen went on to finish the paragraph like this:

While wearing bike helmets does take away some freedom, children should still have to wear helmets. A bad bike crash can badly injure or even kill a child. Losing a small amount of freedom is a small price to pay to keep children from being injured or killed.

So, Gwen showed that she can understand a main argument against her opinion, but she also showed why her opinion is stronger. You should do the same in your persuasive paper.

In your own words, explain one of the main arguments against your opinion.

_____

_____

_____

_____

Now explain why your opinion is stronger.

_____

_____

_____

_____

## Planning Your Paper

Like any report, a persuasive paper has these familiar parts:

1. An introduction, in which you get the reader's attention and tell what you will be writing about.

2. A body, in which you develop your main points, each in a separate paragraph. Each paragraph should have a topic sentence, followed by facts and details to support the topic sentence.

3. A conclusion, in which you wrap up your topic and bring your essay to a satisfying close.

The body of your essay will be made up of a paragraph on each of your subtopics. On page 43, you made a list of subtopics. Has your list changed since you have done your research?

Gwen started out with these three subtopics:

1. Facts about bicycle accidents

2. Facts about how helmets save lives

3. Helmet laws needed in all states

After she finished her research, she added one more subtopic. This subtopic deals with the opposite opinion she read about:

4. Having to wear a helmet takes away some freedom but is worth it.

So, the body of Gwen's essay will have four paragraphs. In each paragraph she will discuss one subtopic at a time.

## Using an Outline

Do you remember preparing an outline when you wrote your report? Now you will use an outline to plan your persuasive paper.

Your outline can follow this model:

I. Introduction

   II. Body

   A. Subtopic

      1. Supporting fact or detail

      2. Supporting fact or detail

      3. Supporting fact or detail

   B. Subtopic

      1. Supporting fact or detail

      2. Supporting fact or detail

      3. Supporting fact or detail

   C. Subtopic

      1. Supporting fact or detail

      2. Supporting fact or detail

      3. Supporting fact or detail

  III. Conclusion

Your outline may have more or less than three subtopics, and more or less than three supporting facts or details per subtopic.

Look at how Gwen completed her outline for one of her subtopics:

   C. Helmet laws needed in all states

      1. There is no national helmet law.

      2. Nineteen states and the District of Columbia have helmet laws.

      3. Some local communities have helmet laws.

      4. Helmet laws work: Brain injuries and deaths in cycling accidents are down in New York, New Jersey, and Florida.

      5. All states should pass helmet laws to reduce injuries and deaths.

☑ Now it's your turn to prepare an outline. Start by gathering your note cards and organizing them into separate piles for each subtopic. Then follow the model outline above. Write on a separate sheet of paper.

# LESSON 6

# DRAFTING: Writing the Body

You have come a long way in writing your persuasive paper. You have chosen and narrowed a topic. You have done research and taken notes. You have organized your facts into subtopics and prepared an outline.

Now it is time to begin writing the first draft. Since most of your thinking so far has been about the body of the essay, begin by writing the body. You will come back later to write the introduction and conclusion.

## Writing Good Paragraphs

The body of your paper is made up of paragraphs. Each paragraph should focus on one subtopic in your outline.

## Topic Sentences

Each paragraph should begin with a special sentence that states the subject of the paragraph. This sentence is called the TOPIC SENTENCE.

**WRITER'S WORKSHOP**

**The TOPIC SENTENCE announces the subject of a paragraph.**

## Misfit Sentences

After the topic sentence, every other sentence in a paragraph should add a fact or detail that is directly related to the topic sentence. Watch out for "misfit sentences"—sentences that don't belong in a paragraph because they stray from the topic.

Read the following paragraph from Gwen's first draft, and then follow the instructions below it.

Every state should pass a law that requires people to wear a helmet when riding a bike. Right now there is no national helmet law. Nineteen states and the District of Columbia have helmet laws, and so do some local communities. There is proof that helmet laws work. New York, New Jersey, and Florida all have helmet laws, and brain injuries and deaths in cycling accidents are down in these states. The best helmets have a special foam lining that cushions the impact in a crash. All states should pass helmet laws to reduce injuries and deaths.

1. In your own words, what is the paragraph about?

_____

_____

_____

2. Underline the topic sentence.

3. There is one misfit sentence in the paragraph. Draw a line through it.

## Now It's Your Turn

Now write the first draft of the body of your paper. Follow your outline. Each subtopic in the outline (A, B, C...) will become one paragraph.

Today you are writing a draft of the *body* of your paper. Later you will focus on writing an introduction and conclusion.

Remember to begin each paragraph in the body with a topic sentence, and then finish the paragraph with facts and details from your outline and from your note cards. Be careful not to let any misfit sentences sneak into your paragraphs.

Double-space when you write your draft. This will make it easier to revise later.

# DRAFTING: Writing the Introduction and Conclusion

## Writing the Introduction

You probably know that an introduction to an essay has two important jobs:

1. It announces the topic (the main idea) of the paper.

2. It catches the attention of readers, making them want to read further.

There are many good ways to write an introduction. Some possibilities include:

• A question

• A striking quotation

• An unusual fact

• A vivid description

• A surprising statistic (a number that tells something important about the topic)

Gwen tried writing two introductions. Here, she used a statistic:

Every year, almost 800 Americans die in bicycle accidents. But 680 of those people would still be alive today if they had been wearing a bicycle helmet. It's a fact that bicycle helmets prevent injuries and save lives. That is why everyone should have to wear a helmet when riding a bike.

Here, Gwen used part of the paragraph that she wrote about the personal experience behind her topic.

One day last summer, my friend Mara was riding down the street on her bike. As she crossed a driveway, a car backed out. The car

hit her back wheel. Mara flew off the bike and hit her head. She was scraped and bruised, but she was all right, because she was wearing a helmet. That helmet saved my friend's life. Every day, helmets save the lives of many bike riders. That is why everyone should have to wear a helmet when riding a bike.

Which of Gwen's introductions do you think is more effective? Why? Pick the introduction you prefer and do the following:

1. Underline the words that state the topic (or main idea) of her paper.
2. Use a colored pencil or highlighter to mark the words that you think might capture the reader's attention.

☑ Now it's your turn to write an introduction. Write on a separate sheet of paper, and double-space when you write.

## Writing the Conclusion

Just one more paragraph to go! Your conclusion should restate the topic of your paper (the opinion you are trying to persuade readers to accept). It also should make readers think more about your topic. It may even urge them to take some action.

The CONCLUSION of a persuasive paper restates the paper's topic. It also tries to make the reader remember what the writer said.

Here is the conclusion Gwen wrote. Read it aloud and then follow the instructions below it.

Even the most careful bike rider can't always stop an accident. If an accident does happen, a helmet is the best protection. In states with helmet laws, there are fewer brain injuries and deaths in cycling accidents. If your state has a helmet law, be sure to obey it. If it doesn't, try to get a helmet law passed. For their own safety, people should have to wear helmets when they ride bikes.

1. Underline the words that restate Gwen's topic (the opinion she wants her readers to agree with).
2. Use a colored pencil or highlighter to mark the words that ask the reader to take action.

☑ Now write your conclusion. Write on a separate sheet of paper and double-space when you write. Remember to do these two things:
1. Restate the topic of your persuasive paper.
2. Give your readers something they will remember.
(If you like, you can also ask readers to take some action.)

# REVISING: Improving Your Content, Plan, and Sentences

You've completed your first draft! Now it's time to make your persuasive paper even better. When writers improve their paper, we say that they are REVISING.

**When writers finish their first draft, they REVISE (improve) their paper.**

## REVISING: Your Content and Plan

Here is a checklist to help you decide on changes to make in the content and plan of your persuasive paper.

|  | Good | Could Be Better |
|---|---|---|
| **MY PAPER'S CONTENT** | | |
| My introduction is interesting and clearly states my topic. | ____ | ____ |
| My facts are strong enough to convince readers to agree with my opinion. | ____ | ____ |
| My conclusion gives readers something to remember. | ____ | ____ |
| **MY PAPER'S PLAN** | | |
| Each of my paragraphs includes only one subtopic. | ____ | ____ |
| Each paragraph of my body has a topic sentence. | ____ | ____ |
| All of the facts in each paragraph fit the topic sentence. | ____ | ____ |

✓ If you have checked "Could Be Better" for any of the items on the checklist, fix that part of your paper. Keep revising until you can check "Good" for every item.

## REVISING: Improving Your Sentences

Before athletes take part in sports, they exercise to build their strength and skills. Here are some exercises that will build your skills for improving the sentences in your persuasive paper.

### Sentences That Are Too Long

Sentences that are too long can be confusing. Try to break long sentences into shorter ones that are easier to understand.

Here is a paragraph written by Matt. Matt's writing is interesting, but he puts too much detail into one long sentence.

> My neighbor's dog bites and my aunt's cats scratch, and my cousins own a bad-tempered yakking monkey and gerbils keep you awake all night running around in those little plastic wheels of theirs and I know this for a fact because my family baby-sat two of them one summer for a friend who went on vacation. Now aren't you convinced that the best kind of pet to own would be a fish?

Here is the way Matt's friend, Anne, rewrote his paragraph:

> My neighbor's dog bites. My aunt's cats scratch. My cousin's monkey is a bad-tempered, chattering pest. The gerbils my family took care of one summer kept us awake all night running around and around in their little plastic wheels. If you're going to have a pet, wouldn't you rather have a nice quiet fish?

Into how many sentences did Anne break Matt's one long sentence? Did you also notice that she used sentences of different lengths? Underline two short sentences that Anne wrote. Put brackets [  ] around Anne's longest sentence. Put parentheses (  ) around two medium-length sentences.

Now it's your turn. Here is a paragraph from Rosa's paper. It is just one long—*very long*—sentence. See if you can break Rosa's paragraph into sentences of different lengths. Rewrite the paragraph on the lines.

I should have a phone of my own because it's hard when my mom and dad and brother and sister tie up the line and even though I understand that everyone needs to use the phone it upsets me waiting for them to get off the phone when I'm expecting an important phone call and need to use the phone.

_____

_____

_____

_____

_____

_____

_____

_____

_____

✓ Look at your persuasive paper. Does it contain sentences that are too long? If so, make several smaller sentences.

### Sentences That Are Too Short

Did you ever ride a bus that stopped at every single corner? That kind of ride can be jerky. The same thing is true of using too many short sentences. It makes the reader feel as if you are "putting on the brakes" too often. Here is an example:

The man was a construction worker. He wore an orange vest. He wore a hard hat. He was using a heavy tool called a jackhammer. He was working on the new highway. His gloves had holes in them. He looked cold.

Here is how Anne rewote the paragraph to make it smoother:

The construction worker wore an orange vest and a hard hat. His gloves had holes in them. Although he looked cold, he pounded away at the new highway with his heavy jackhammer.

Here are some ways to combine short, choppy sentences. Read each example. Then use the same method to combine the sentences that follow the example.

1. Put describing words (adjectives) together.

    Example: I like big, loud trucks.

I bought a tropical fish. It was beautiful. It had stripes.

_____

_____

_____

2. Join sentences together with "and."

> Example: My brother made some pizza and some salad.

I bought some popcorn. I also bought a hot dog.

_____

_____

3. Use another joining word (as, so, since, because, when, if).

> Example: My feet were wet, so I changed my socks.

I wanted a new bike. Mine was old and rusty.

_____

_____

Now rewrite the paragraph below on the lines that follow it. Combine some of the short sentences.

I like rock music. It is loud. It is fun. I like the beat. I like the words to the songs. I wish my parents liked it more. But they don't. I use my earphones.

_____

_____

_____

_____

✓ Now take a good look at your own paper. Does it contain sentences that are short and choppy? If so, make some of them longer sentences.

# LESSON 9

## PROOFREADING/PUBLISHING: Finishing Your Paper

Your paper is almost finished! After you give it one final checkup, it will be time to make your final copy. One problem you should look out for is called a RUN-ON SENTENCE.

Many people have trouble with run-on sentences. A run-on sentence does not have to be long. A run-on is really *two sentences written as if they were one.*

Compare the sentences below :

CORRECT  Ants spoiled the picnic when they crawled on the food.

RUN–ON  Ants spoiled the picnic, they crawled on the food.

Run-ons can be fixed by dividing them into two sentences, or by joining them together correctly with joining words. Fix the run-on sentences below by using joining words from the following list:

but     and     because     since     when     so     if     after     although

1. Wet dogs are smelly, I like them anyway.

_____

_____

2. Fish make good pets they are quiet and gentle.

_____

_____

3. Try to do it yourself, if you can't, ask for help.

_____

_____

✓ Before you make the final copy of your persuasive paper, use the checklist below. If you can't honestly put a check in each blank space, make the changes that are needed. Then copy your paper neatly. You will want your paper to be "dressed in its best" when you share it with your readers.

## Content

_____ Will my introduction catch readers' attention and encourage them to continue reading?

_____ Does the body of my paper use enough facts and examples to explain my opinion clearly?

_____ Does my conclusion restate my main idea and give the reader something to remember?

## Good Writing

_____ Does my persuasive paper follow a clear plan or outline?

_____ Is each of my paragraphs about only one subtopic?

_____ Do all the facts in each paragraph fit the topic sentence?

_____ Did I use sentences of different lengths?

## Correctness

_____ Did I avoid run-on sentences?

_____ Does each sentence begin with a capital letter?

_____ Have I indented the first word of each paragraph?

_____ Does each sentence end with the correct punctuation mark?

_____ Are all of my words spelled correctly?

# WRITING NEWS ARTICLES

## LESSON 1

## PREWRITING: Reading News Articles

"Have you heard the news?" When we're asked that question, most of us open our eyes and ears. We like to know what's going on around us. That's one reason so many of us read newspapers.

Newspapers bring readers the daily history that we call THE NEWS. The dictionary defines *news* as "reports of recent happenings; matters of interest to newspaper readers." City newspapers report on local, state, national, and international news.

Newspapers have four main purposes:

1. to INFORM readers through general news articles;

2. to INTERPRET (explain news and its probable effects) through editorials;

3. to SERVE readers through listings of local meetings, weather, births, deaths, television schedules, advice columns, and advertisements;

4. to ENTERTAIN through feature stories, comics, and crossword puzzles.

In this unit, you will work with the first purpose listed above. You will learn to write a NEWS ARTICLE.

Can you explain the difference between a news article and an editorial? (Hint: Both contain facts, but only one includes the writer's opinion.) Try to finish the definitions below.

1. A(n) _____ describes a recent happening that is of interest to readers.

2. A(n) _____ expresses a writer's opinion about a current event or situation.

## News Articles

In this unit, you'll learn to write news articles that are fair, accurate, and complete. You must be careful to use only facts—not your own opinions.

Read the following example of a news article that might be found in a local newspaper. Then answer the questions that follow the article.

### SOCCER PLAYERS RAISE FUNDS FOR ANIMAL SHELTER

Players in all levels of the Jefferson Area Youth Soccer League participated in a weekend campaign at McIntire Park on November 2-3 to raise money for the Have-a-Heart Animal Shelter, recently in danger of closing due to lack of funds.

Pee-Wee League players raised over $500 in a "best-dressed pet" contest. Recreational League players held a bake sale, while the Chllenge League held a car wash. The Super Strikers travel team sponsored a 5-kilometer run.

In all, over $5000 was raised for the shelter, which provides free lodging and medical care for injured and abandoned animals.

Melissa Gant and Josh Barnett, co-captains of the Super Strikers, organized the fundraising effort. "When we heard the shelter needed money," said Gant, "we wanted to help. We started out by asking our friends, but then the whole soccer league got involved."

Shelter director Marcy Percy says that the players' efforts will keep the shelter open for many months. She also said the fundraising drive has raised awareness of the shelter's needs, and more pledges of support are coming in.

1. WHO did something in this article? _____

_____

2. WHAT did they do? _____

_____

3. WHERE did they do it? _____

4. WHEN did they do it? _____

5. WHY did they do it? _____

_____

6. HOW did they do it? _____

_____

_____

## Facts and Opinions

Remember the first purpose of a newspaper? It is to INFORM the readers. General news articles carry out this purpose. When you report news, you should give just the facts. Don't write anything that is your own opinion. The editorial page is the place for opinions.

**WRITER'S WORKSHOP**

**A news article should use only FACTS. Opinions should not be included.**

A FACT is something that has actually happened or that can be proved to be true. An OPINION is something that someone *believes* to be true. An example of a fact: *The manager reported that 632 people bought tickets to the concert.* An opinion: *This was the best concert of the year.*

Read the sentences below. Label each statement *F* (fact) or *O* (opinion).

_____ 1. The children performed in a musical on Tuesday, May 3.

_____ 2. The movie is better than the book.

_____ 3. Mrs. Ling bakes the best cookies in the world.

_____ 4. Basketball practice is held at 3 P.M. on Fridays.

_____ 5. Summer vacation should be longer.

_____ 6. Mrs. Brown's pet shop has an aquarium.

_____ 7. Our town needs a new shopping center.

✓ In a journal or on a separate sheet of paper, list some current events that you might like to write about. Then indicate whether you would write a news article or an opinion about each one.

# PRWRITING: Identifying the Five W's and How

I keep six honest serving men;
(They taught me all I knew.)
Their names are *What* and *Why* and *When*
and *How* and *Where* and *Who*.

from "The Elephant's Child"—*Just So Stories*
by Rudyard Kipling

The opening sentences of a news article are called the LEAD. The lead answers most or all of the six questions that Kipling included in his poem. These questions are sometimes called "the Five W's and How." Newswriters answer them in their leads so that readers can quickly learn the most important facts about news events.

A LEAD for a news article answers the most important questions about the story: WHO, WHAT, WHERE, WHEN, and sometimes WHY and HOW.

Read the following lead and then answer the questions about the Five W's and How:

Tom Tortoise defeated Howie Hare in a race through the Fabled Forest early yesterday afternoon. While Hare paused and fell asleep, Tortoise kept up a steady pace and achieved a surprising victory.

Who: _____

What: _____

When: _____

Where: _____

Why: _____

How: _____

## Writing a Lead

**WRITER'S WORKSHOP**

A LEAD should get the reader's attention and include most of the Five W's and How.

There are many ways to write a lead for a news article. Here are a few:

**Summary.** Use a few words that describe (or sum up) the whole event: *Last night's basketball game between Clearview and Stonewood was a close one. The final score was 43–42 at the Clearview Gym.*

**Quotation.** Start with a quotation from someone involved in the story: *"It was a wet but wonderful experience," Tom Bell said of his raft trip down the Colorado River last summer.*

**Description.** Describe the scene where the event took place: *A ferris wheel with brightly colored lights, game booths filled with shouting people, and cotton candy on the faces of little kids—all of these are part of the carnival being held at Lincoln Park this week.*

**Question.** Ask an interesting question to catch the reader's attention: *Why does Mrs. Johnson look so healthy this year? It may be because she spent her summer vacation at a fitness camp.*

When a newspaper reporter writes a story, she uses her notes, mostly gathered from observing the events or interviewing people who know what happened. Here are some notes for a story Gina was asked to write about a child who rescued a dog. Choose the facts that tell who, what, where, when, why, and

how. Write a lead for her story about the dog rescue. Remember, a lead has only the MOST IMPORTANT facts that tell the Five W's and How. Leave the other facts and details for the rest of the story.

dog named Lindy

rescuer: Henry Perlman, age 9

Henry: brown hair, blue eyes

Henry walking in Ashburn Park yesterday

Lindy: English springer spaniel friendly, likes to chase squirrels

2 years old, brown and white

Henry heard Lindy whining

Lindy belongs to Schuster family on Parkway Ave.

dog owners bought dog as puppy

Henry found Lindy with collar caught in wire fence

dog had been missing overnight

Henry unbuckled collar to free Lindy

Henry freed Lindy, took her to owners listed on tag

_____

_____

_____

_____

_____

_____

# PREWRITING: Planning the Rest of the Article

A news article can be compared to an upside-down pyramid:

**Lead:** Most important information.
Answers WHO, WHAT, WHERE, WHEN,
sometimes WHY and HOW

**Body:** Next most
important information

Least important
details

In the article below, draw a circle around the LEAD. Which sentences do you think make up the most important information in the BODY?

What is a stingy old miser like Scrooge doing in our town, and why is he singing? Parkwood residents will find out on December 7 when the Children's Theater Group performs a musical version of "A Christmas Carol" at the Langley Auditorium.

Performances will run nightly at 7:30 through December 22. To reserve seats, call 555-9876.

Parkwood mayor Danny Toscano plays the role of Scrooge. All other roles are performed by actors from ages two to twelve in the Children's Theater Group.

"I've never acted or sung onstage before, but the kids make me feel right at home," said Toscano.

"Mr. Mayor makes a good Scrooge, even when he sings," said Jamal Jackson, age six, who plays Tiny Tim.

## Headlines

A headline for a news article is like a title for a story. It tells what the article is about. When you look at a newspaper, you will see that every article has a headline. Newspaper readers read the headlines to find out which articles they want to read. Remember these hints for writing good headlines:

1. Make them short.
2. Don't use *a*, *an*, *and*, or *the*.
3. Use action verbs.
4. Don't use periods or full sentences.
5. Use an important fact from the story.
6. Make them catchy to get readers' attention.

Discuss the headlines below. Which are the best for news articles?

1. HURRICANE FORCES EVACUATION OF JONES BEACH

2. THERE ARE TOO MANY COMMERCIALS ON TV

3. SUPER STRIKERS CAPTURE CHAMPIONSHIP

4. A TRIP TO THE ZOO IS A FUN WAY TO SPEND A DAY.

5. OFF-DUTY POLICEMAN FOILS ROBBERY

Now, on the lines below, write two headlines for the news story on page 69. When you have finished, use the hints at the top of this page to check your headlines. Choose the one that best fits the rules and that you like best.

_____

_____

_____

_____

_____

_____

# DRAFTING: Writing a News Article from Given Facts

Below are the steps for writing a news article when you have gathered all the facts. Read the instructions carefully. Then follow them, step by step, as you complete the activity on the next page. Check off each step as you complete it.

_____ Step 1: Read through all the facts.

_____ Step 2: Find the WHO, WHAT, WHERE, WHEN, WHY, and HOW facts on the next page and label them on the blank spaces.

_____ Step 3: Write these facts into your LEAD. Remember that the lead can be a sentence or a paragraph. Use complete sentences. Don't use the personal pronouns *you*, *I*, *me*, *we*, or *us*. Use past tense unless the news event is in the future.

_____ Step 4: After you are satisfied with your lead, decide on (and mark with an *X*) the other facts you want to include. You may not want to use all facts you have been given.

_____ Step 5: Now write the BODY of your article from the facts you checked.

_____ Step 6: Check to be sure you've included all the important facts. Cross out facts as you use them to help you stay organized.

_____ Step 7: Write a headline for the article. Make it short and interesting, using important words from the lead.

_____ Step 8: Add your name (BYLINE) under the headline. (This is a special privilege for a newspaper writer.)

✓ On another sheet of paper, write a news article using the facts below. (The facts aren't in the order you will use them.) Follow the steps, one at a time, described on page 71. Skip lines as you write so that you will have space to make changes.

_____ 1. Book Fair—sale of used paperback books

_____ 2. books of all types: adventure, science fiction, biography, historical fiction, mystery, realistic fiction

_____ 3. sale will be held September 21–24

_____ 4. will be held in Northside Library

_____ 5. Northside Library address—1791 Wexler Avenue

_____ 6. sponsored by Parkwood Reading Buddies

_____ 7. time of sale: 8 A.M.–2 P.M.

_____ 8. literacy tutors and volunteers will work at the fair

_____ 9. fair open to everyone

_____ 10. fair will raise money for Reading Buddies tutoring program

**WRITER'S WORKSHOP**

Newswriters first find the Five W's and How, and write them into the LEAD. Then they combine the remaining information into the BODY of the story. Least important details are written last.

# PREWRITING: Gathering the News

Before you can write your own news article, you'll need to gather information. There are three main ways to gather news. First, whenever possible, ATTEND the event you are reporting. Second, INTERVIEW people who have a part in the story or who know what happened. Third, read or RESEARCH background information about your article.

## Attending the Event

Seeing the action yourself is best whenever you can. Be sure to take notes on what you see and hear. Write down not only what happens, but also the looks, sounds, and mood of the event.

If you were reporting on a sports awards banquet, you would need to get a list of the awards and those who received them. You also might describe the decorations, the excitement of the crowd, the reaction of those who got awards, the speech of the coach, and anything else you observed.

✔ Imagine that a famous author of children's books will visit your local library next week to read from his or her latest book. On the lines below, write down the kind of information you might include in your notes.

Facts: _____

Quotes from: _____

Description: _____

Other: _____

## Interviewing

If you can, try to arrange to speak with someone who knows a lot about the topic of your news article. If you go prepared with good questions and ready to listen, then an interview can be a great source of information for your news article.

To prepare for an interview, carefully read the following steps:

1. *Make an appointment with the person.* Be sure to explain the reason for the interview. Begin and end the interview on time.

2. *Make a list of questions to ask.* Prepare more than you think you'll need, just to be safe. Don't ask questions that could be answered with "yes" or "no." If you think of a new question during the interview, ask it, even though it's not on your list.

3. *Remember to be pleasant and polite.* Stay on the subject of your news article. Don't express your own opinions. (You are there to ask questions, not to tell what you think.) Let the other person do most of the talking.

4. *Take careful notes.* If you want to QUOTE (use the exact words of) the person, be sure you have written them down correctly. Read the words back to the person to make sure.

5. *Don't rely on a tape recorder for your notes.* You may take a small recorder with you, if the person you are interviewing agrees. If you use a tape recorder, take notes also, just to be safe.

6. *Ask for the correct spelling of names.* Read them back to the person you are interviewing. Remember that accuracy is very important.

7. *Thank the person for the interview.*

8. *Rewrite your notes as soon as possible after the interview.* It is hard to remember what your notes mean if you wait too long.

✔ Read the following list of questions for interviewing a model airplane maker. Then think of someone you could interview, and use the rest of the page to make a list of questions you might ask.

1. What is the exact name of the award you have just won?

2. How did you get started making model planes?

3. How long have you been making them?

4. How many different kinds of planes can you make?

5. Would you describe one or two of your favorites?

6. What is the highest award a person can win for making model planes?

7. How are the planes judged?

8. How does a person learn to make them? Are there books or classes?

9. Do you fly your planes? How long can one stay up?

10. What do you enjoy most about your hobby?

Questions for My Interview with _____

About _____

_____

_____

_____

_____

_____

_____

_____

_____

## Researching Background Information

It is always good to have some background information for your news article. Before you attend an event or interview someone, find out all you can about the subject from encyclopedias, books, magazines, and other sources.

Below is an article about "tinikling," a dance that comes from the Philippines. Which parts of the story do you think the writer may have learned from research?

### JUMPING THE STICKS
#### By April Peterson

"Swish, step, crack!" Those are the sounds of tinikling, a favorite dance at Parkwood community Center. The yearly tinikling contest will be held in the Community Center on May 13.

For the past six years, Parkwood mayor Danny Toscano, who lived in the Philippines 15 years ago, has taught free classes in tinikling. "It's a dance that requires some athletic ability, but even if you can't do it, it's fun to watch," said Toscano. Over the years, some Parkwood residents have improved their skills by learning more difficult dance steps and gymnastics. For the past few years, the Community Center has held a tinikling contest with pizzas for the winners.

Tinikling began in the Philippines. It was named after the long-legged "tikling" birds that hop between tall reeds and branches.

Tinikling dance steps are done between quickly moving sticks. The sticks are moved to a special rhythm by other dancers.

In the Philippines, girl tiniklers wear colorful wraparound skirts and loose blouses with butterfly sleeves. Boys wear brightly colored pants with one leg rolled up. They also wear long-sleeved shirts and bright scarves. Tiniklers often dance barefoot.

## Choosing an Event to Report

Until now, you have been learning about reporting the news. Now, it's your turn to be the reporter. You will plan, gather facts for, and write a news story of your own.

First, choose an event that is coming up in your community. The event should be one that you'll enjoy or in which you have a special interest. Here are some ideas:

a baseball game (or other sport)    a contest

a festival    a fun run

a fundraiser    a parade

a Scout meeting    a special visit

On the lines below, write the information about the event you will attend:

Name of event: _____

The event happens where: _____

The event happens when: _____

People I could interview to find out more about the event:

Name: _____

Where and when I can talk to this person: _____

_____

Name: _____

Where and when I can talk to this person: _____

_____

I can find out background information:

About what subject: _____

From what sources: _____

Use this information to gather information for your story.

# Using Quotations

As you work on gathering information, you will be writing what people tell you. When someone says something interesting, write his or her exact words. If the person says something really interesting, then you can quote those words in your article. Using a quotation from someone you interview can make a story come alive for your readers.

## Using Direct Quotations

When you use someone's exact words, you place quotation marks around them. This way of quoting someone is called a DIRECT QUOTATION. For example:

"Honestly, I never thought I'd win first prize in the Science Fair," Sam Michaels said.

"Every cent we raise today will go directly to the animal shelter," said Coach Jane Duvall.

Here are some rules for using quotation marks:

• Place quotation marks only around the *exact* words the person said.

• Use a comma to separate the quoted words from the words that explain who is speaking. In general, punctuation marks—such as the period, comma, question mark, or exclamation point—go *inside* the quotation marks. For example:

"I understand," Marcie said.

"Do you really understand?" I asked Marcie.

"I told you, I understand!" Marcie yelled.

Then Marcie said, "I'm sorry, I didn't mean to yell."

• You can place the quotation at the beginning or end of a sentence, or even in the middle.

### At the beginning:

*"No one knows Paris as well as I do," Mr. Couteau said.*

Notice that you capitalize the first word of the quotation and use a comma to separate the quoted words from the rest of the sentence. And notice that the comma goes *inside* the closing quotation mark.

***At the end:***

*Mr. Couteau said, "No one knows Paris as well as I do."*

Again, you capitalize the first word of the quotation and use a comma to separate the quoted words from the rest of the sentence. In this case, notice that the comma comes *before* the opening quotation mark.

***In the middle:***

*"No one," Mr. Couteau said, "knows Paris as well as I do."*

Notice that the second part of the quotation (beginning with *knows*) does *not* begin with a capital letter. Pay special attention to where to place the two commas.

The sentences below have problems with punctuation. Rewrite each sentence on the lines below it to correct the problem or problems.

1. "What is the total "? Mr. Hill asked.

_____

_____

2. We expect the musical performance to be a highlight of the weekend." Brent Satter said.

_____

_____

3. "I really wish" Sandra Hecht told the crowd "That you could have heard him speak."

_____

_____

4. "Better safe than sorry" the clown said, just before he landed in the bucket.

_____

_____

5. My father always told me "do your best, and then do a little more".

_____

_____

## Using Indirect Quotations

An INDIRECT QUOTATION reports what a person said without using his or her exact words. It is not enclosed in quotation marks. Contrast the following direct and indirect quotations.

DIRECT:     "Honestly, I never thought I'd win first prize in the Science Fair," Sam Michaels said.

INDIRECT:   Sam Michaels said he never thought he would win first prize in the science fair.

DIRECT:     "Every cent we raise today will go directly to the animal shelter," said Coach Jane Duvall.

INDIRECT:   Coach Jane Duvall noted that all the money the team raises will go to help the animal shelter.

Here are some direct quotations. Rewrite them as indirect quotations. Remember that when you write an indirect quotation, you do not use the exact words of the person you are quoting.

1. "I know our team will win," Melody Jacobs said. "We have the best players in the city."

_____

_____

2. "I thank each and every person who has contributed to the fund to help buy books for the Mexican school," Violet Garza said.

_____

_____

3. "My pet alligator keeps burglars away," said Safari Jane.

_____

_____

4. Mr. Grant claimed, "My experience makes me the best candidate for mayor."

_____

_____

5. "One balloon drifted all the way to Kentucky," reported Mike Malone.

_____

_____

# Examining Newspaper Style

Some things about writing a newspaper article are a little different from other writing you have done. For example, there's the lead. In a newspaper article, you make sure you say the most important facts first.

There are some other things you should keep in mind as you plan and write your story.

## Be Brief and to the Point

Use short paragraphs and sentences. Omit unnecessary words. Try to get the most information in the least space. Newspapers are meant to be read quickly.

The sentences below are too long for a newspaper story. See if you can make them shorter. Try to find a shorter way to express the words in the parentheses. Use proofreading marks to change the sentences. (The first sentence has been done as an example.)

1. The Parkwood basketball teams (~~took part in~~) *held* a bake sale (~~for the purpose of~~ *to* raising) money (~~to pay~~ for) a new scoreboard.

2. Mr. Wong, (who is the new coach), (is a man who) is interested in (the sport of sailing).

3. (The people who attended the program) learned facts (that were interesting) about hunger (in the world).

4. Mrs. Jefferson (made the statement that) the (recently built) pool was (of great length).

## Avoid Redundant Words

A redundant (rih-DUN-dunt) word repeats a thought that has already been expressed in another word or words in the sentence. For example:

*The firemen climbed up the ladder.*

To "climb" is to "go up." There is a hidden "up" in the word "climb." So, to say "climb up" is to be redundant.

Cross out the redundant words in the sentences below.

1. They lowered down the drawbridge.     2. Would you repeat that again?

3. Mr. Warren has got a lot of money.

*Always be accurate.* Reporters must check and double-check their information. Readers trust the printed words of a newspaper. They expect reporters to be accurate and fair.

Think how you would feel if a story were written about you. You would be very excited as you opened your paper to read about yourself. What would you think if the first thing you saw was your name—spelled incorrectly? Of, what if the reporter wrote something that you did not say?

Below is a paragraph from a news article. It contains five errors. Can you find and correct them? You might want to use an encyclopedia or almanac to check the information.

Mr. Long is from Chacago, the capital of Illinois. He is a fan of the Red Sox, his hometown baseball team. Chicago's nickname is "the Snowy City." It is a port city on Lake Huron.

# DRAFTING: Writing the First Draft of Your Article

You have taken notes, gathered your information, and planned what you want to say. Now it's time to write your article!

## Review Your Notes

Collect all your notes, including any interview notes. Read through them before you start to write.

You will probably not need to use everything you have written in your notes. As you read through your notes, think about which facts and details are the most important. Those are the ones you should use in your news article.

As you read through your notes, do these two things:

1. Use a highlighter or colored pencil to mark any facts that answer the questions *who*, *what*, *where*, *when*, *why*, and *how*.

2. With a regular pencil, underline any other important facts or details that you think you will want to include in your article. If you took notes on an interview, underline any sentences you think you might want to use as a direct or indirect quotation in your article.

## Make a Quick Plan

Planning a news article is a little different from planning other kinds of writing. You don't need to write a formal outline. And you don't have to plan paragraphs that each begin with a topic sentence, although the information in each paragraph should stick to a single topic. Still, you do need a plan that moves from the most important information to the least.

Let's look again at the article you read a while ago:

### SOCCER PLAYERS RAISE FUNDS FOR ANIMAL SHELTER

Players in all levels of the Jefferson Area Youth Soccer League participated in a weekend campaign at McIntire Park on November 2-3 to raise money for the Have-a-Heart Animal Shelter, recently in danger of closing due to lack of funds.

Pee-Wee League players raised over $500 in a "best-dressed pet" contest. Recreational League players held a bake sale, while the Chllenge League held a car wash. The Super Strikers travel team sponsored a 5-kilometer run.

In all, over $5000 was raised for the shelter, which provides free lodging and medical care for injured and abandoned animals.

Melissa Gant and Josh Barnett, co-captains of the Super Strikers, organized the fundraising effort. "When we heard the shelter needed money," said Gant, "we wanted to help. We started out by asking our friends, but then the whole soccer league got involved."

Shelter director Marcy Percy says that the players' efforts will keep the shelter open for many months. She also said the fundraising drive has raised awareness of the shelter's needs, and more pledges of support are coming in.

Here is how a plan for that article might look.

1. Lead

2. What each league did

3. Total amount raised

4. Quotations from the main organizers, Barnett and Gant

5. Information from interview with director Marcy Percy

To plan your article, look back over your notes and try to think of the main points you want to make. Write the points in a numbered list, with one number for each paragraph. You don't need to write complete sentences. Quick notes will do.

Write your plan here. Or, if you have more points, use a separate sheet of paper.

1. Lead _____

2. _____

3. _____

4. _____

5. _____

## Writing the Lead

A news article begins with the lead. This beginning paragraph gives your readers the most important information right up front.

Look at your notes. You used a highlighter or colored pencil to mark the facts that answer the "Five W's and How" questions. Use those facts to fill in the lines below. (If you don't have "why" and "how" facts, that's all right. They don't apply to every news article.)

WHO: _____

_____

WHAT: _____

_____

WHEN: _____

_____

WHERE: _____

_____

WHY: _____

_____

HOW: _____

_____

✓ Use the answers you just wrote to help you write your lead. A lead should get your reader's attention, but most of all it should tell what the article is about by answering many of the "Five W's and How" questions.

Write your lead on a separate sheet of paper. Skip a space between each line.

### Writing the Body of the Article

Once you have written your lead, you can write the rest of your first draft. Keep these tips in mind as you write the body of your article:

- Skip a space between each line so you have room to revise.
- Follow your plan (the numbered list of main points). As you write, you might find that it makes more sense to use a different main point or change the order of your plan. That's fine. Let your plan help you, not tie you down.
- Think of yourself as the reader. What would you want to know next?
- Write the information from the most important to the least important.
- Include quotations to add interest.
- Keep your paragraphs and sentences short.
- Once you finish your first draft, look over your notes to make sure you did not leave out any important facts.
- Last but not least, write a headline for your news article. Make it short and interesting enough to catch your reader's interest, and make sure it communicates the most important point in your article.

# REVISING: Improving Your News Article

## Revise for Content

Reporters who write for a living go through the same steps you are going through to write a news article. One of the most important of these is revising.

When you revise a news article, you are looking for many of the same things you look for in any writing. You want your writing to be clear to your reader. You want your reader to understand the point of your writing. Use this checklist to help you make changes in your news story.

_____ Does my lead contain the most important facts: *who, what, where, when,* and possibly *why* and *how*?

_____ Will my lead capture the interest of the reader?

_____ Does the body of my article contain additional facts?

_____ Did I use only facts, no opinions?

_____ Is my headline short and interesting?

_____ Does my headline contain important ideas from my lead?

You can make other improvements to your news article. Writers choose exact words for the meaning they want, and they make sure that all of their sentences make sense. They remove unnecessary words. They try to make their sentences "flow," or read smoothly. Below are some other ways to improve your news article.

## Think About Your Audience

Whenever you write, you must consider your AUDIENCE (the people who will read your article). Because news stories are read by people on many reading levels, it is best to write simply. This is not the time to use all the big words you may know.

The sentences below contain some hard words. See if you can replace those words with words that are easier to understand. (The first big word has been changed as an example.) Then look over your news story to see if you have used

hard words unnecessarily. If you have, replace them with easier words.

1. Jeremy ~~is capable of~~ swim~~ming.~~ _can_
2. Mr. Mason contemplated his answer.
3. Sarah made a preferable choice.
4. The trip originated in Boston.
5. The carpenter constructed the house.
6. The boy consumed his cereal.
7. Mrs. Mote relocated the desk.

**WRITER'S WORKSHOP**

**Your AUDIENCE is the people who read your writing. Be sure to use words they will understand.**

## Begin Sentences in Different Ways

You can make your writing more interesting by beginning sentences in different ways. Try not to use the same word to start several sentences in a row. One easy way to change your beginning word is to switch the second half of the sentence with the first. For example:

The sun's rays shone brightly inside the kitchen.
Inside the kitchen, the sun's rays shone brightly.

A line of soldiers marched along the edge of the forest.
Along the edge of the forest, a line of soldiers marched.

Here are sentences for you to try. Rewrite each one with a different beginning.

1. The Siamese cats crept silently along the narrow brick wall.

_____

2. The children huddled near the fire during the snowstorm.

_____

## News Stories in Review

Fill in the blanks below to review some of the words used in this unit. If you need hints, unscramble the letters underneath the blanks.

1. A news article contains facts, not the writer's _____ .
   *nipooni*

2. The opening sentences of a news article are called the _____ .
   *edla*

3. The news questions are _____ , _____ , _____ ,
   *ohw,*        *athw,*        *ewehr,*

   _____ , and sometimes _____ and _____ .
   *nehw,*              *woh*              *hwy.*

4. The least important details come at the _____ of a news article.
   *den*

5. The title of a news story is called its _____ .
   *alhnieed*

6. To _____ means to change and improve your writing.
   *veresi*

7. Reporters ask people questions during an _____ .
   *ritewinev*

8. Looking up facts in the library is called _____ .
   *saerrech*

9. The people who read a news story are called its _____ .
   *neidecua*

# PROOFREADING/PUBLISHING: Checking Your News Article

Remember that reporters check and recheck to be sure an article is interesting, complete, and accurate.

The following checklist will help you decide if your writing is ready for publication.

_____ Is my headline short and interesting? Does it tell an important fact?

_____ Does my lead contain answers to the news questions *who*, *what*, *where*, *when*, and sometimes *why* and *how*?

_____ Will my lead catch the attention of the reader?

_____ Does the body of my article contain other facts, with the least important details at the end?

_____ Was I careful to use only facts (not opinions), and did I check my facts for accuracy?

_____ Does my article contain short sentences and paragraphs with a variety of sentence beginnings?

_____ Did I use clear, simple language?

_____ Have I checked my sentences for incorrect grammar?

_____ Is my spelling correct?

_____ Do all sentences and proper names begin with a capital letter?

_____ Have I checked my sentences for incorrect grammar?

_____ Is my spelling correct?

_____ Do all sentences and proper names begin with a capital letter?

_____ Is all my punctuation correct, including punctuation of any quotations?

✓ Make a final copy of your news story.

# OPTIONAL: WRITING A PLAY

## PREWRITING: What Is a Play?

What does the word *play* make you think of? A game? Something that you do just for fun? Why do you suppose the same word is used to mean "a story that is acted out"? People have always enjoyed watching each other act out plays.

Sometimes the events acted out were happy ones like weddings, parties, or victories. Sometimes they were not so happy: crimes, family problems, disasters, even death.

Today, as in ages past, we still enjoy seeing stories acted out. In other words, we still enjoy watching plays.

**A PLAY is a story that is acted out.**

In this unit, you'll write a short play of your own.

### Plays and Stories

If you've written stories, you know they are made up of three main ingredients (or ELEMENTS). These elements are PLOT, CHARACTERS, and SETTING.

The matching activity below will help you define PLOT, CHARACTERS, and SETTING.

_____ 1. Plot

A. the PEOPLE that things happen to in a story

_____ 2. Characters

B. the PLACE and TIME in which the story happens

_____ 3. Setting

C. the PLAN for the things that happen in a story

Like stories, plays have plots, characters, and settings. But plays are different from stories in some other ways. To learn some of those differences, look at the following two ways of writing about the same event. The first was written as a story. The second was written as a part of a play. Read both versions carefully.

### A Fly in the Soup (A Very Short Story)

The Space Rock Cafe was busy as usual on Saturday afternoon. The waiter wound his way through the crowd and set a large bowl in front of Darvac.

Darvac was starved. She grabbed the spoon and thrust it into the soup. "Wait a minute," she said. "There's a fly in my soup!" She angrily waved her spoon in the air. "Hey, waiter! What's a fly doing in my soup?"

The waiter walked by, carrying a tray. "That," he said nonchalantly, "is the backstroke, I believe."

### A Fly in the Soup (A Very Short Play)

Setting: _Crowded cafe in outer space. Various species of space creatures are seated at tables, enjoying a Saturday afternoon lunch. A waiter is bringing a bowl of soup to Darvac, sitting at a table upstage._

DARVAC (_Grabbing a spoon_): Ahhh, it's about time. I'm starved.

WAITER: Enjoy your lunch, ma'am.

DARVAC (_Surprised_): Wait a minute! There's a fly in my soup. (_Angrily waving the spoon in the air_) Hey, waiter! What's a fly doing in my soup?

WAITER (_In a bored way_): That is the backstroke, I believe.

How is the little play you just read different from the story? Answer the following questions:

1. In the story, how do you know what the setting is?

   _____

   _____

2. In the play, how do you know what the setting is?

   _____

   _____

3. How are the exact words of the characters written in the story?

   _____

   _____

4. How are exact words written in the play?

   _____

   _____

5. How do we know that Darvac is angry in the story?

   _____

   _____

6. How do we know that she is angry in the play?

   _____

   _____

✔ Think of a funny story or joke that has two people talking to each other. Write the story on another sheet of paper.

### Discussing the Two Kinds of Writing in a Play

The play about the Space Rock Cafe told its story mainly through the words of its characters. We call these words the DIALOGUE of a play. Underline an example of dialogue in the play on page 92.

Both the play and the story take place in the Space Rock Cafe somewhere in outer space. In other words, the SETTING for each of them is "the Space Rock Cafe in outer space."

Look back at page 92. Put parentheses ( ) around some words in the story that tell us its setting (both time and place). Put brackets [ ] around the words in the play that give us the same information.

The writer also gives other instructions to the actors throughout the play. We call these statements STAGE DIRECTIONS. Stage directions tell the actors what to do (grab a spoon, wave, speak angrily).

In the play on page 92, circle at least two examples of stage directions.

**The story of a play is told through two kinds of writing: DIALOGUE and STAGE DIRECTIONS.**

### Let's Try It!

✓ On the next page, you'll see a paragraph from a short story. Read it carefully. Then rewrite it as part of a play. Remember to describe the *setting* at the beginning. Tell the rest of the story by writing *dialogue* and *stage directions*. Some of the play has been written for you. The underlined words in the story will give you some hints.

## The Treasure

Jenny and Dan crept to the back of the cave. If they had read the map correctly, a bag of gold was hidden somewhere near the back wall. Dan directed the flashlight up and down, back and forth. <u>Jenny pointed to a pile of rocks.</u> They carefully moved the rocks, one at a time. Suddenly <u>Dan saw an old wooden box.</u>

Setting: _____

_____

_____

DAN (*Shining the flashlight up and down on the cave wall*): According to the map, the bag of gold is hidden back here somewhere.

JENNY: _____

_____

_____

_____

DAN: _____

_____

_____

_____

# PREWRITING: Writing Dialogue

Little children make up dialogue when they play pretend games. They just make up what they think the characters would say. People who write plays do the same thing.

For example, suppose you were having trouble with a friend. Your friend wants to go to the movies. But you want to do something else that you enjoy very much, such as riding bikes or going swimming.

What words do you think your friend would use to tell you he or she wanted to go

to the movies? _____

_____

What would you answer? _____

_____

Then what would your friend say? _____

_____

Now write that *dialogue* as if it were in a play.

YOUR FRIEND: _____

_____

YOU: _____

_____

YOUR FRIEND: _____

_____

## Writing Dialogue

Write some dialogue to turn the paragraph below into a scene from a play. (Don't write the stage directions just yet.) Look for words like *told*, *said*, *repeated*, to find out what the characters said.

In a play, when you are writing DIALOGUE, write the name of the person who is speaking in capital letters, followed by a colon ( : ). Don't use quotation marks ( " " ).

## Fishing at Indian Lake

One sunny morning in July, my uncle and I went fishing at Indian Lake. Almost as soon as I put my line in the water, I felt a big tug. I hollered, "Uncle Marty! I've got a big one!" He told me to keep calm and just reel it in. I told him I couldn't wait to see what was on the line, and he repeated his advice to keep cool. I told him I would try, but my heart was pounding.

_____

_____

_____

_____

_____

_____

✓ Look at the funny story or joke you wrote. Write some dialogue for the characters.

# PREWRITING: Writing Stage Directions

Every play has two kinds of STAGE DIRECTION: 1) setting directions at the beginning, and 2) stage directions sprinkled throughout the play.

## Setting Directions

The SETTING DIRECTIONS give instructions for the scenery and other things (dishes, books, furniture) that show the setting to the audience. They also tell which characters are "onstage," and when the action is taking place. Remember this example?

Setting: *Crowded cafe in outer space. Various species of space creatures are seated at tables, enjoying a Saturday afternoon lunch. A waiter is bringing a bowl of soup to Darvac, sitting at a table upstage.*

On the lines below, write some setting directions for the play *Fishing at Indian Lake* on page 97. Describe where and when the action takes place.

Setting: _____

_____

_____

## Other Stage Directions

The other stage directions are sprinkled throughout the play. These directions tell the actors:

1. what actions to take with their bodies,
2. what expression to have on their faces, or
3. how their voices should sound (for example, angry or happy).

**98**

Some examples of stage directions are below. On the blank before each example, write the number of the kind of stage directions (from page 98) that it is.

_____ DARVAC *(Grabbing a spoon)*: Ahhh, it's about time. I'm starved.

_____ DARVAC *(Surprised)*: Wait a minute! There's a fly in my soup.

_____ WAITER *(In a bored way)*: That is the backstroke, I believe.

Reread *Fishing at Indian Lake* on page 97. Think about the actions the characters would be taking. Also think about the expression on their faces and the tone of voice in which they would speak. Then use carets ( ∧ ) to add some stage directions to the dialogue you wrote below the paragraph.

## More Practice

Now write some setting and stage directions for the paragraph below. Use carets ( ∧ ) to put stage directions in the dialogue at the bottom of the page.

Tony waited impatiently at the bus stop. People were crowding around, getting ready to stampede when the bus came. "If it ever comes," Tony thought. He shivered a little in the brisk winter and kicked a soft drink can along the curb.

Setting: _____

_____

MAN: Where is that bus? When it comes, I'm going to bawl out the driver.

TONY: If it ever comes!

✓ Now add stage directions to the funny story or joke you wrote dialogue for.

# PREWRITING: Turning a Famous Story into a Play, Part 1

Today you will begin to turn a famous story into a play. You'll start by deciding on a famous story you think would make a good play. Then list the characters in the story and give a brief description of each one. For example, let's use a familliar childhood story, "Little Red Riding Hood." You would write:

LITTLE RED RIDING HOOD, a gentle little girl on her way through the woods to visit her grandma

THE BIG BAD WOLF, a mean, sneaky wolf who disguises himself as Little Red Riding Hood's grandmother

THE WOODSMAN, a good man who saves Little Red Riding Hood from the wolf

On the line below, write the name of the famous story you have decided to change into a play.

_____

Now write the main characters in this story.

_____

_____

_____

_____

_____

_____

Before you decide which events from your story to change into a play, let's talk about the word *scene*. A scene is a part of a play that takes place in one setting and in one period of time. When the action in a play moves from one place to another, we say that the "scene changes." When the play jumps from one time to another, we also say that the scene changes.

Here is a way to find an exciting event to turn into a scene in a play. In the column on the left below, list the main events in the story you chose. In the column on the right, briefly describe the setting in which each event takes place.

Events                                          Settings

_____          _____

_____          _____

_____          _____

_____          _____

_____          _____

_____          _____

_____          _____

_____          _____

☑ Now choose some events that would make good scenes for a play. Put stars beside the events you pick.

## The Tiger Stories

Here is the beginning of a play that a student wrote based on an African folktale. The story tells about a tricky character named Anansi.

Notice how the play begins with a list of characters. Then look at how the

writer used dialogue and stage directions. You might enjoy reading this scene aloud with friends or family members.

CHARACTERS

ANANSI, a spider

TIGER, the king of the jungle

SMALL ANIMAL, Tiger's servant

QUEEN BEE, the ruler of the bees

ANT

### SCENE 1

Setting: *In the heart of the jungle.*

*(Tiger is seated on a throne. Small Animal scurries onstage and crouches beside him.)*

SMALL ANIMAL *(Gasping)*: Oh, King Tiger, I thought of some more. There is the tiger-lilly, the tiger-moth, and, of course, the Tiger Stories! *(Finally out of breath)* Yes, your Greatness, all of those wonderful things are named after you.

TIGER *(With an air of smug satisfaction)*: It is good. Say them again. I always like to hear them. *(Small Animal takes a deep breath and is about to begin when Anansi enters.)*

ANANSI: Oh, mighty Tiger, please forgive me, but I could not help overhearing all the things that are named after you. There are so many tiger-names that sometimes I think you ought to build a palace to keep them all in.

TIGER: It is a good idea, my many-legged friend. Perhaps I will build a palace where the animals can hear my names spoken all day long. Now come sit by me. You, too, may listen to all my names. *(Small Animal takes another deep breath, ready to begin.)*

ANANSI: Oh, great Tiger, I know your names very well. I can almost recite them all. But, great Tiger, with so many names, won't you give one to a poor little creature like me? May not one thing bear the name of Spider?

TIGER *(Laughing)*: Well, Anansi, I see no harm in naming something after a creature as small and weak as you. As long as it is not one of my great names.

ANANSI: I will not ask for one of your great names, O honored tiger. Give me only the Tiger Stories. Let the stories be named after me. Let them be called Spider Stories.

SMALL ANIMAL *(With an excited squeak)*: Oh! Oh no! That is Tiger's favorite name. It is the greatest name of them all. Only the wisest animal in the jungle can have that name. Pick something else to bear your name, Anansi—anything but the stories!

# DRAFTING: Turning a Famous Story into a Play, Part 2

Today you will DRAMATIZE the events you chose from your story. That is, you will turn them into scenes from a play.

Writing or acting out an event as a scene from a play is called DRAMATIZING it.

Before you write your events in play form (with dialogue and stage directions), you'll need to answer some questions. Use the form below.

Scene 1

1.  What happens in this scene? (Describe briefly.)

_____

_____

_____

2.  What can the characters SAY to show what is happening?

_____

_____

_____

3. What can the characters DO to show what is happening?

_____

_____

_____

4. How can you let the audience know about things that are happening offstage (where the audience can't see them)?

_____

_____

_____

☑ Now use the answers you have written to turn an event (or events) from your story into a scene (or scenes) from a play. Begin by describing the SETTING. (Include where and when the scene takes place, as well as all the CHARACTERS that are in the scene.) Then finish the scene by using DIALOGUE and STAGE DIRECTIONS. Write the scene on your own sheet of paper.

When you've finished, use the checklist below to decide if you need to make changes.

| Scene Checklist | Good | Could Be Better |
|---|---|---|
| I have described the time and the place and listed each character in the setting directions. | | |
| Everything that happens in the scene is explained to the audience by the dialogue or the stage directions. | | |
| Things that happen offstage are explained by dialogue or sounds. | | |

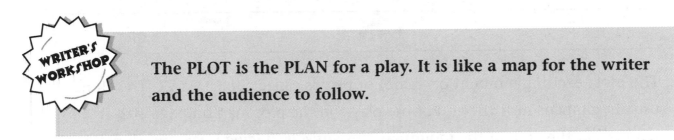

# DRAFTING: Identifying the Plot of a Play

Like most good writers, a playwright makes an outline or plan for a play. This plan is called the PLOT of the play.

**WRITER'S WORKSHOP**

**The PLOT is the PLAN for a play. It is like a map for the writer and the audience to follow.**

One plot that is used over and over in plays is like a map for climbing a mountain. It looks like this:

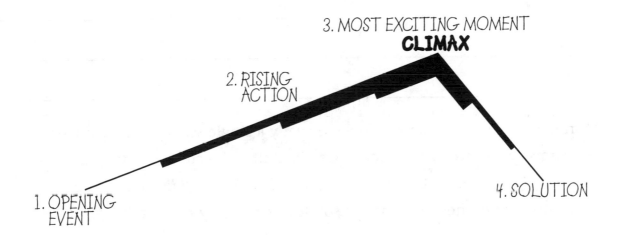

3. MOST EXCITING MOMENT
CLIMAX

2. RISING ACTION

1. OPENING EVENT

4. SOLUTION

Let's look at each part of that plan:

1. The play begins with an OPENING EVENT. In the opening event of *Little Red Riding Hood*, her mother asks her to take some goodies to Grandma. On the lines, describe the opening event of the story you are dramatizing.

_____

_____

_____

2. The middle of the play includes events that become more and more exciting. These events are called the RISING ACTION. In *Little Red Riding Hood,* the meeting with the wolf in the woods and at Grandma's house make up the rising action. What events make up the rising action of the story you chose?

_____

_____

_____

3. The most exciting moment of a story or play is called the CLIMAX. The climax usually happens near the end of the play. On the plot map on page 102, it happens at the "top of the mountain." In *Little Red Riding Hood,* the climax is when the wolf says, "The better to eat you with, my dear!" What is the climax of the story you chose?

_____

_____

_____

4. Stories and plays also have sections (usually a single scene) in which their problems are solved. This scene takes place after the climax. Let's call it the SOLUTION SCENE. In the solution scene of *Little Red Riding Hood,* the Woodsman saves her. What is the solution scene in your story?

_____

_____

_____

☑ Read the opening scene from your play again. Then write another scene or scenes for the rising action and the climax.

# REVISING: Talking More About Dialogue

You know that much of a play is told through the words of its characters, and you've written some dialogue. Now it's time to learn some of the special ways dialogue can be used in a play.

Remember that a play is different from a story in some ways. Story writers can *tell* readers what characters are like. They can write sentences like this one: *The king was evil.* The writer of a play can't do that. He or she must tell everything through stage directions or dialogue. Look at all the jobs a writer can do with dialogue:

1. Move the story along.

2. Tell what kind of people the characters are.

3. Tell about the setting.

4. Let us know what is happening offstage.

The following speech from a play does all four of the jobs listed above. Read it carefully and answer the questions about it on page 108.

OLD MAN: My hair may have turned to silver, but I'm sure of one thing. When my younger brother comes tonight to take my throne, I will fight fiercely. My castle is crumbling, but its walls are still thick enough to stop that evil fiend. Even now, while he and his men are crossing the rain-drenched field to the east of my castle, my knights are preparing for the battle. My wicked brother may win this fight, but—mark my words—he'll do it over my dead body!

1. What dialogue moves the story along by telling you what things are happening or are going to happen?

_____

_____

_____

2. What dialogue tells what the king is like?

_____

_____

3. What dialogue describes the king's brother?

_____

_____

4. What dialogue tells about the setting?

_____

_____

5. What dialogue tells you what is happening offstage?

_____

_____

☑ Look at the dialogue in the scenes you have written so far. Does it do some of the jobs described by this lesson? If you see ways to improve the dialogue, go ahead and make the changes. Then go on to write the solution scene to your play. When you finish that, you will have a complete draft of your play!

# REVISING: Thinking More About Characters

In real life, it takes a long time to get to know people well—to find out what kind of characters they really are. In plays (and other kinds of stories) we get to know the characters much more quickly. That is because writers have special ways of letting us know what characters are like.

As a writer of plays, you'll use at least four ways to show the audience what a character is like. These methods include:

1. Giving stage directions for the way the character should be dressed.

2. Giving stage directions for the way the character should act.

3. Writing words for the character to say that tell us something about him or her.

4. Having another character say something that tells us what a character is like.

The following scene uses all four ways to tell the audience about a character. In each blank space, write the number (from above) of the method you think the writer has used.

MOTHER: Whose turn is it to take out the trash?

FATHER: Billy's.

SISTER: You should have known. Better call him or it'll still be here in the

morning. _____

FATHER: Billy! Come here and take out the trash!

(Billy enters the kitchen. He is wearing blue jeans and a shirt that is only half-way

buttoned. He is barefooted.) _____

FATHER (Firmly): Billy, take out the trash. It has been sitting here all day!

BILLY: Sorry, Dad. I guess I forgot again. _____

(Billy quickly puts on his winter jacket, zips it up, grabs the trash bag, and heads for

the door, still barefooted.) _____

☑ Now think back to the play you wrote from a famous story. Choose one of the characters from that play, and think of a word or words to describe that character in some important way. (Maybe the character is forgetful like Billy. Maybe he or she is mean, kind, sneaky, brave, or funny.) Write the word that describes your character on the line below.

My character is _____

Now think of some ways to let the audience know what your character is like.

1. The character could wear _____

_____

_____

_____

2. The character could (do something) _____

_____

_____

_____

3. The character could say _____

_____

_____

_____

4. Another character could say _____

_____

_____

_____

# REVISING/PROOFREADING/PUBLISHING: Finishing Your Play

☑ Use the checklist below to decide on changes to make in your play. When you're sure your play is as good as you can make it, copy it neatly on a new sheet of paper.

## Characters

Do we learn enough about each character through:

_____ his or her words?

_____ things he or she does?

_____ things other characters say?

## Plot

_____ Is what's happening—the plot—easy for the audience to follow?

_____ Is the story told mainly through the dialogue?

_____ Do the stage directions make the action clear to the audience?

## Setting

_____ Are the time and place described clearly in the setting directions?

## The Form of the Play

_____ Is each character's name in capital letters, followed by a colon?

_____ Are all stage directions underlined and enclosed in parentheses ( )?

Congratulations! You are now a playwright. Like most writers, you're probably looking forward to seeing your play acted out. Ask friends and family members to help bring your play to life. Have fun!

# Writing an Original Play

You have written a play based on a familiar story. If you've been bitten by the playwriting bug, then you might want to try writing an original play. ("Original" means fresh, new, and not based on something else.) Begin by using the matching activity below to review the elements and parts of a play.

**Let's Review**

_____ 1. plot       a. the people or creatures the story happens to

_____ 2. characters       b. a part of a play that takes place in one setting and one period of time

_____ 3. setting       c. the words the characters say in the play

_____ 4. stage directions       d. the time and place in which the story happens

_____ 5. dialogue       e. instructions from the writer about what the characters should do and how they should look

_____ 6. scene       f. the events that take place in the story

**Ready? Let's Go!**

Think of a problem that your play could be about. Here are some examples.

1. *A girl finds a secret tunnel to a hideout where some jewel thieves are hiding.*

2. *A boy must find homes for seven kittens or they'll have to go to the pound.*

3. *A girl builds a robot, but it refuses to obey her.*

Choose one of the ideas above or think of one of your own. Write it here:

_____

_____

_____

Next, think of the characters you will need to turn the problem you have chosen into a play. List them below, and write a brief description of each character. How does he or she talk, act, and look?

1. _____

   _____

2. _____

   _____

3. _____

   _____

4. _____

   _____

Now think of the SETTING in which your play will take place. Will it be in your own backyard, on a train, in a dark tunnel, in an attic, at the beach? You decide. Then write and describe it here:

SETTING: _____

_____

_____

Next, make a list of the *things that will happen* in your play—the events that will make up the PLOT. Write them below:

_____

_____

_____

Look at the events you have decided to include in your plot. How many SCENES will you need to tell the story? (Remember that a scene is a part of a play that takes place in one setting, without jumping from one time to another.) You may need only one scene, or you may need two or three. On the lines below, write what will happen in each scene of your play (use the events from the list above).

SCENE 1: _____

_____

_____

_____

SCENE 2: _____

_____

_____

_____

SCENE 3: _____

_____

_____

_____

Now begin writing your play, one scene at a time, on your own sheet of paper. Use the form of the play that begins below as a guide. Remember the rules:

1. When characters speak, write their name in capital letters, followed by a colon (:) .
2. Put stage directions in parentheses ( ) and underline them.

✓ Read Lesson 6 again. Do the events in your play build up to the climax? Is the climax really exciting? Is the solution satisfying? Make any changes that will make your play more exciting.